ELECTC
REGIST___
1832 - 1948;
and Burgess Rolls:
A Directory to Holdings
in Great Britain

Jeremy Gibson

Introduction by
Colin Rogers

The Family History Partnership

2008

Published 2008 by
The Family History Partnership,
PO Box 502,
Bury, Lancashire BL8 9EP

Email: sales@thefamilyhistorypartnership.com
Webpage: www.thefamilyhistorypartnership.com

This replaces *Electoral Registers since 1832*, Gibson and Rogers,
1989, 1990

ISBN 978 1 906280 08 6

Cover illustration: 'Working men voting during the dinner hour', from *The Illustrated London News*, February 1874 (the first general election after the passing of the Ballot Act of 1872), reproduced by kind permission of the Greater London History Library.

Typeset in Arial by the compiler.
Printed by the Alden Press, Witney, Oxon.

In Memoriam

DON STEEL
1935 - 2008

CONTENTS

PREFACE

Almost two decades ago Dr Colin Rogers and I produced two 'Gibson Guides', to *Poll Books* and to *Electoral Registers from 1832*. Both have been out of print for many years. A new, fourth, edition of the former is being published simultaneously with this, totally new, Guide.

However, with *Electoral Registers*, developments have called for a new approach. Perhaps the most significant has been the need to restrict this by concluding at 1948, whereas before we continued up to the date of publication. Since 1948 there have been numerous boundary changes resulting in old constituencies disappearing and new ones coming into existence. Due to concerns about availability of personal information (which is what family and local history is all about) there are, today, restrictions on access to current electoral registers. It is hoped that 1948 will seem sufficiently distant not to warrant concern on this account.

This depressing attitude apart, the new approach has been made possible by the publication, by the British Library in 1998, of Richard H.A. Cheffin's monumental work *Parliamentary Constituencies since 1832* (a new edition is in preparation). This provides a very detailed catalogue of the holdings of the British Library, which even then spread over two miles of shelving. In the earlier Guide we were only able to include what turned out to be stray registers that had appeared in the Library's main catalogue. The official series was catalogued separately. With the willing agreement of the British Library, this new Guide includes all (up to 1948) of this unique and gigantic collection.

The British Library catalogue was arranged by constituency, in strict alphabetical order, from 'Abbey – see Westminster' to 'Zetland – see Orkney and'. Whilst this new Guide retains the usual 'Gibson Guide' arrangement by pre-1974 counties of England and Wales (Scotland is fully alphabetical), each county is now arranged, first, by the County constituen   cies, followed by the Borough constituencies. Within these two categories, they are arranged by the periods started and terminated by boundary changes. These were: **1832** to **1867**; **1867**-**1885** (many had no change until 1885); **1885** to **1918** (but there were no registers for 1915-1917); and **1918** to **1948** (again with none for war years, 1940-44). The further major boundary change, in 1948, provides a logical finishing point. This Guide now makes it clear when constituencies of the same name expanded or at least changed the area which they covered. Many small Boroughs lost their status in 1885, but may have continued then or later as the name of a Division of their County.

This has made it possible to list and differentiate all the constituencies up to 1948, and show exactly what survive of the annual printed registers. It is all too easily assumed that if a register was in print there must be copies surviving. In fact the British (Museum) Library only started acquiring *all* registers after World War 2; and much the same is true of the National Libraries of Wales and Scotland. Pre-1914 registers are often surprisingly sparse and many are missing entirely. Thus fortuitiously surviving registers may turn out to be unique – such as some of those around 1874 that are found in The National Archives. It is hoped that this Guide, which shows exactly what is known to survive in libraries and record offices, will bring to light others in unsuspected collections.

My colleague Dr Colin Rogers has kindly allowed me to use the (updated) Introduction he wrote for our former Guide. As much of his interest is in the registers of more recent years, the responsibility for the listing that appears here is mine alone.

INTRODUCTION

Colin Rogers

Registers of Parliamentary electors were the creation of the 1832 Representation of the People (or 'Reform') Act (2 Will.IV c.45), their significance ever since being that a voter's name must be on them in order that a vote may be cast. They have been compiled annually since 1832, except 1916-17 and 1940-44 inclusive (when the most recent register, or the National Register of 1939, was taken as the basis of the electorate), and 1919-1926 and 1945-1949 (when registers were compiled twice a year). Until recently the public has always been able to inspect them, as a check for accuracy, and to purchase copies.

Content

Electoral registers have never been simply a list of voters' names. Until the 1918 Representation of the People Act ('RPA', 7 & 8 Geo.V c.64), the register included the qualification which brought each on to the register: current residence, ownership of property in the constituency or polling district, and tenancies of those properties which were not self-occupied (see illustration). Handwritten annotations can be found in some extant registers giving, e.g., voting intentions, or actual votes cast, death or removal, or agents' observations. Also distinguished (since the amalgamation of Parliamentary and local government registers, from 1878 in boroughs, 1885 elsewhere) were those who are entitled to vote in one and not the other. Peers, for example, could vote locally, but not in national Parliamentary elections. Those no longer qualified for jury service, being over the age of 65, are not normally so identified in public copies, only in those supplied to the courts, but sometimes lists of those so qualified have survived, and have been included in this Guide if they have been reported to us. Similarly we have incorporated some lists of freemen, accepted in some periods as a qualification to vote, but they should not be taken as a complete guide to all, or indeed any, in any one repository.

Abbreviations have been used in Electoral Registers from time to time. 'D' indicates a voter not enfranchised for local government elections; 'L' indicates a voter not enfranchised for Parliamentary elections; 'M' refers to a merchant seaman; 'S' is a service (military) voter; and 'Y' is one who would reach the age of 21 in the first half of the year in which the register is in force, used from 1928 to 1970. This Guide only covers registers to 1948. Subsequent developments, reduction in age of voting to 18, the arrival of the European parliament, abolition of hereditary peerage are ignored.

Draft registers, or 'Lists', were drawn up by Overseers (in county constituencies) or Town Clerks (in boroughs), for most of the nineteenth century, and even when Electoral Registration Officers were instituted, overseers could still be asked to provide the basic lists of names. Final registers are the result of amendments to this draft, resulting from appeals and objections, or other relevant data such as knowledge of a voter's death or (until 1918) local authority rate books.

During the nineteenth century, the registers are in alphabetical order of voters' names within each polling district, but the 1884 Act brought the registers of voters in Parliamentary and local government elections so closely in line that the street order of burgesses could be adopted. Even so, burgess lists are often to be found separate from the electoral register until the First World War. The 1918 RPA laid down that,

Christian Name and Surname of each Voter.	Place of Abode.	Nature of Qualification.	Street, Lane, or other like Place in this Parish, where the Property is situate; or name of the Property, or Name of the Tenant.
NO.			
4069 Walker James	Rowde	freehold houses	Himself and others
4070 Weston Stephen	Rowde	freehold house and garden	Rowde

Parish of WEST LAVINGTON, and Tythings of LITTLETON PANNELL and FIDDINGTON, in the Hundred of Potterne and Cannings.

4071 Alexander Charles	Littleton Pannell	lands, as occupier	Littleton farm
4072 Baker Joseph	West Lavington	freehold house	Fiddington
4073 Baker George	West Lavington	freehold land	Fiddington
4074 Baker William	Littleton mill	mill and land, as occupier	Littleton mill
4075 Box Richard	Little Chiverell	freehold lands	Fiddington
4076 Brown John	Littleton Pannell	freehold house and lands	Himself
4077 Brown James, senior	Littleton Pannell	freehold houses and lands	Himself
4078 Box Thomas	Market Lavington	freehold land	Fiddington
4079 Blake Robert	West Lavington	copyhold house and land	Himself
4080 Beckett William Turner	Wantage, Berks	freehold land and mill	Thomas Newman & another
4081 Caswall Robert C.	West Lavington	freehold house and land	Himself
4082 Chapman Richard	Littleton Pannell	freehold house and land	Himself and others
4083 Chapman Richard	Littleton Pannell	freehold land	Fiddington
4084 Chapman James	Littleton Pannell	freehold house and land	Himself and others
4085 Chapman William	West Lavington	freehold house and garden	Himself and others
4086 Coleman Robert	Black Dog Inn	house and land, as occupier	West Lavington
4087 Dark Stephen, senior	West Lavington	land, as occupier	West Lavington
4088 Davis Thomas	Littleton Pannell	freehold house and land	Himself
4089 Giles John	Littleton Pannell	freehold house and land	Littleton Pannell
4090 Giles James	Littleton Pannell	freehold house and land	Himself
4091 Hale Raymond Jones	Fiddington farm	land, as occupier	Fiddington farm
4092 Hibbert Joseph	Littleton Pannell	freehold house and land	Jeremiah Nusland
4093 Holmes John	Little Chiverell	freehold house and land	Henry Gray
4094 Hibberd James	Littleton Pannell	freehold house and land	Himself
4095 Hooper Harry	West Lavington	land, as occupier	Yanger's bottom farm
152			

A page from the 1841 Electoral Register for West Lavington in Wiltshire. This political agent's annotations provide details of electors to whom he had evidently lodged objectons, with some success.

wherever possible, the register should be published in street order ('cadastrally', as one librarian reminded us). In recent decades, but long after 1948, computerisation has enabled lists to be produced alphabetically and in street order. However, other events have led to them being 'embargoed' for ten years or even longer (see Rogers, 1986).

Age of Voters

Until reduced to 18 by the 1969 Registration of the People Act (Eliz.II c.15), effectively from 1971, the age of voting was 21 and above, the only exception being soldiers and sailors of 19 and 20 at the end of the First World War. By the 1918 RPA women of 30 or over were enfranchised, extended to 21 and over by the 1928 RP (Equal Franchise) Act (18 & 19 Geo.V c.12).

Qualifications to vote

In counties, the right to vote was given in 1429 to all men of 21 or over having freehold lands or tenements whose annual net value was 40s. or more; until 1774, such voters had to reside in the county in which that land or tenement was situated. The pre-1832 franchise in Scotland was narrower than in England and Wales, as the county '40s.' freehold was taken as the value as it has been at the end of the thirteenth century, and increased through inflation to some £70.

The 1832 Reform Act (2 & 3 Will.IV c.45) extended the county franchise by giving the vote to:

a) anyone having a life interest in, and occupation of, lands or tenements worth over £2 and under £5 per annum;

b) all other holders of real property worth at least £10, a figure reduced to £5 by the 1867 Reform Act (30 & 31 V. c.102); 1867 also gave the vote to occupiers (owners or tenants) of lands of the rateable value of £12 or more, and paying poor rates; and

c) occupiers, as tenants, of lands or tenements paying rent of £50 per annum or more.

In boroughs before 1832, the franchise varied widely according to local custom, an extensive electorate in Preston, for example, contrasting with that in the 'pocket boroughs' such as Old Sarum, Wiltshire, where the M.P. was elected by only eleven voters in 1802-3, or seemingly-populous 'rotten boroughs', such as Banbury, where the franchise was confined to the eighteen members of the corporation. In Scotland, the burgh vote was limited solely to a delegate nominated by each burgh council.

The 1832 Act standardised this franchise, and rather more than doubled the number of voters to just under one million. The right to vote was given to owners or tenants of buildings worth at least £10 per annum, provided they had occupied it/them for at least twelve months prior to the registration date (15 July annually) and that the appropriate poor rates and assessed taxes had been paid. Residence within seven miles of the borough was essential. This franchise was extended in 1867 to all owners and tenants of dwelling houses (or part thereof if separately rated) and to lodgers paying at least £10 per annum who had lived there for at least twelve months. The 1867 Act should not be underestimated, as it probably increased the electorate by a greater percentage than any other Reform Act, particularly in the boroughs, adding some one and a half million voters to the register.

In 1884, freeholders of inherited land (or land acquired by marriage) worth 40s; freeholders of any land worth £5; and certain lessees, occupiers and lodgers, were enfranchised. Thus, the borough qualification which had so extended the franchise in 1867 was now applied to the counties. The Act created about three million new voters,

OXFORDSHIRE
BANBURY PARLIAMENTARY DIVISION
HANBOROUGH POLLING DISTRICT — T

Hanborough
Northleigh

REGISTER OF ELECTORS
1918

DIVISION I contains the names of those persons who are entitled to vote both as Parliamentary Electors *and* as Local Government Electors.

DIVISION II contains the names of those persons who are entitled to vote as Parliamentary Electors but *not as Local Government Electors*.

DIVISION III contains the names of those persons who are entitled to vote as Local Government Electors but *not as Parliamentary Electors*.

NOTE.— † Persons against whose names the mark † is placed are not entitled to vote in respect of that entry at Elections of County Councillors.

‡ Persons against whose names the mark ‡ is placed are not entitled to vote in respect of that entry at Elections of Rural District Councillors *or* Guardians.

§ Persons against whose names the mark § is placed are not entitled to vote in respect of that entry in the case of a Borough or Urban District at Elections for Borough or District Councillors as the case may be, and in the case of a Parish at Elections for Parish Councillors or at Parish Meetings.

* Persons against whose names the mark * is placed will vote at another polling place at Parliamentary Elections.

a Persons against whose names the letter *a* is placed are Absent Voters.

In the fourth column the following abbreviations are used :—

R. = Residence qualification.　　　　HO. = Qualification through husband's
BP. = Business premises qualification.　　　　occupation.
O. = Occupation qualification.　　　　NM. = Naval or Military Voter.

PARISH OF HANBOROUGH

HANBOROUGH POLLING DISTRICT—T　EYNSHAM ELECTORAL DIVISION

DIVISION II — *continued*

(1) No.	(2) Names in full. Surname first.	(3) Residence or Property occupied and abode of non-resident occupier.	(4) Qualification.
418	*a*Lay, Hubert Michael	The Bakery	N M
419	*a*Lay, Walter James	Church Hanborough	N M
420	*a*Long, Alfred	Long Hanborough	N M
421	*a*Long, John	Burleigh Row	N M
422	Long, Ernest	Church Hanborough	R
423	*a*Long, Lewis	Mill Wood End	N M
424	Long, Andrew	Park Lane	R
425	Long, John	Do.	R
426	*a*Mansell, James	Opposite Manor Farm	N M
427	*a*Mansell, John Clarke	Church Hanborough	N M
428	*a*Martin, William	Opposite George Inn	N M
429	*a*Martin, George Thomas	Do.	N M
430	*a*Martin, Ernest	Do.	N M
431	*a*Martin, William Thomas	Bassett Road	N M

ABSENT VOTERS' LIST. OXFORDSHIRE. BANBURY PARLIAMENTARY DIVISION.

1 No.	2 Names in Full (Surname first).	3 Qualifying Premises.	4 Description of Service. Ship, Regiment, Number, Rank, Rating, &c., or recorded address.	5 No.
	PARISH OF HANBOROUGH.—*Continued.*			
3911	Leech, Thomas Henry	Park Lane	45562 Pte. R. Berks	3911
3912	Long, Alfred	Long Hanborough	14430 Pte. 1/4th Wilts	3912
3913	Long, John	Burleigh Row	129334 Gnr. R.G.A.	3913
3914	Long, Lewis	Mill Wood End	3197　A.V.C.	3914
3915	Long, William	Park Lane	Pte. R.G.A.	3915
3916	Mansell, James	Opposite Manor Farm	920086 Gnr. R.F.A.	3916
3917	Mansell, John Clarke	Church Hanborough	026074 Pte. A.O.C.	3917
3918	Mansell, Mark Alvin	Near Manor Farm	R.A.F.	3918
3919	Martin, Ernest	Opposite George Inn	14029 Pte. 7th O.B.L.I.	3919
3920	Martin, George Thomas	Do.	201777 Pte. 1/4th O.B.L.I.	3920
3921	Martin, William	Do.	S/215645 Pte. A.S.C.	3921

The 1918 Electoral Register for Hanborough in Oxfordshire, showing examples from both the main list and the Absent Voters List (reproduced by kind permission of Oxfordshire Record Office).

especially in country areas. Despite the reforms, however, by 1911 only some sixty per cent of male adults were registered.

In 1918, the qualification was greatly simplified to those normally resident in the constituency at the qualifying date, those with business qualifications, and graduates of British universities. Women aged 30 or over, who were local government electors or the wives of local government electors, were given the Parliamentary franchise for the first time, increasing the electorate by about six million women, as well as a further three million men. Women over 21 were enfranchised by the 1928 RP (Equal Franchise) Act.

Plural voting

Voters having cause to appear in more than one register (e.g. students living away from home) have always had the right, perhaps the duty, to do so (for an examination of the effect of this phenomenon, see Blewett, 1965). The right to vote in more than one constituency, however, was first curtailed by the 1918 RPA, by which an elector could vote under only two of three headings: residence, business, or university. Our present system of 'one man, one vote' was the residue when the business and university qualifications were abolished by the 1948 RPA.

Absent voters

By the 1918 RPA, members of the armed services were listed separately under the constituencies in which they would normally have appeared. Arrangements were made for temporary absences by both postal and proxy voting systems (see Holding, 1986, for details).

Normally resident adults not qualified to vote in Parliamentary elections

1. Those whose names have (for whatever reasons) been omitted from the register, even if they are otherwise qualified to vote.
2. Aliens, unless naturalised since the 1870 Naturalisation Act (33 & 34 V. c.14).
3. Peers; though Peeresses were deemed qualified by the 1918 RPA, they were specifically disqualified by the 1963 Peerage Act (c.48).
4. Lunatics (though periods of lucidity have been deemed sufficient temporarily to remove this incapacity).
5. Those serving as policemen, and for six months thereafter, until the 1887 Police Disabilities Removal Act (50 & 51 V. c.9).
6. Election agents and others paid to help at elections were given the vote by the 1918 RPA.
7. Those in receipt of public alms (as well as their spouses and children) could not vote until the 1918 RPA (see *Rogers on Elections* for details and difficulties of definition).
8. Postmasters, before 1918.
9. Commissioners and most collectors of government revenues before 1918.
10. Anyone convicted of bribery at elections (for five years thereafter).
11. Anyone serving a prison sentence.
12. World War I conscientious objectors during the period 1918 to 1923.
13. Anyone else not satisfying conditions in force at the time.

Dates

There are three principal dates associated with each register, the 'qualifying date' by which a voter establishes the right to vote in a particular constituency, the date on which the register comes into force, and the date on which the register is replaced by a new one, normally after twelve months. These dates can spread across three calendar years. In the Guide which follows, we have tried to give the availability of surviving registers according to the year in which they came into force. There are many purposes, including genealogy, however, for which the qualifying date is the most meaningful, because it purports to establish ownership, occupation or residence at a particular address on or by that date – many voters have already died or moved when the register comes into force. The changes to the dates that have occurred since 1832 are shown in the table below. These were not always rigorously applied. The 1832 register was brought in on 1 November in several constituencies, and the East Sussex register for 1841 started on 31 October. It must also be borne in mind that different criteria may be used by those supplying the information. Thus apparent discrepancies of a year earlier or later are often to be found. We have not attempted to standardise these.

From	Qualifying date	Date coming into force
1832	31 July	1 December
1843	31 July	30 November
1867	31 July	1 January
1878	15 July	1 January
1885	31 July	1 January
1918	15 January	15 April
	and 15 July (1 June, AVL's)	15 October
1926	15 July	15 October
1928	1 Dec. (15 Dec. Scotland)	1928 1 May 1929
	thereafter 1 June	15 October

For the complicated arrangement after the War, see the 1945 RPA (8 & 9 Geo.VI c.5).

1948	20 Nov. (1 Dec. Scotland)	16 March
	and 15 June	1 October

Local government franchise

Registers of electors for different levels of local government have survived, and may be particularly useful because, at certain times, they contain a greater proportion of the population than the registers of Parliamentary electors, particularly before 1918.

The Guide contains references to registers of voters for County Council elections. These commenced following the 1888 County Electors Act (51 & 52 V. c.10) which defined the franchise for the County Councils established in the same year. The vote was given to all those who had a Parliamentary vote as £10 occupiers, as well as to existing burgess voters.

Burgesses were the electors of the borough councils, their registers often pre-dating the registers of Parliamentary electors, as this Guide shows. Earlier variations were standardised by the 1835 Municipal Corporations Act (5 & 6 Will.IV c.76) to those occupying rateable property for two and a half years, paying rates, and living within seven miles of the borough (defined as road or water routes in 1843). Unmarried women were included in the burgess rolls from 1869, and the occupation qualification reduced to one year. The 1878 Act encouraged Parliamentary and Burgess lists to be drawn up together, so the latter are often in street order after that date.

The 1894 Local Government Act (56 & 57 V. c.73) split off the civil functions of local government at parish level, which had been operated by vestries since the Vestries Acts of 1819 and 1831. Parish Councils were introduced, all ratepayers in the parish having a single vote, and 'registers of parochial electors' were drawn up separately until the First World War.

Also found within the Guide are occasional references to registers of electors for specific local government functions, all of which were later subsumed under the main Council functions – Lighting and Watching from 1830, Poor Law Guardians (1834), Public Health (1848) and School Boards (1870).

Sources of inaccuracies in the registers

Between the qualifying date and the start of the year for which the register is current, many voters will have died, and many others (some five per cent, or higher in urban areas) will no longer be living at the same address, a phenomenon which, it is claimed, has had a deciding influence on some results of elections held late in the year. If the register is being used as a source of addresses to locate an individual in the 1871 census, therefore, it might be more appropriate to look in the 1872 electoral register. The 1878 Parliamentary and Municipal Registration Act (41 & 42 V. c.26) allowed for transfer of data every quarter from Registrars of Death to those compiling electoral registers, but this does not seem to have been particularly effective, possibly because of the cost to the ratepayer, and is still not achieved in most areas even today (for fairly modern estimates of the inadequacies of electoral registers, see Todd and Dodd, 1982).

Correspondingly, individuals will have moved into a constituency after the qualifying date, and are unable to register therein. Until 1928, when the 'Y' system was introduced (see above), voters who were to reach the qualifying age during a register's currency might not have been found on it. Some of the otherwise qualified electorate deliberately chose not to register. This group, common enough in all periods, increased in relatively recent times in a vain attempt to evade the poll tax.

Even without political manipulation, there were many other causes for the non-appearance of those with the franchise (see Rees, 1970, and Seymour, 1970 for details). Rates had to be paid by the qualifying date, for example, though even here, rate collectors were known to trick their political opponents into late payment. Rate collectors sometimes died, leaving late collection inevitable. Rates which were paid through the landlord instead of directly to the local authority could not be included – it has been estimated that half the electorate of Tower Hamlets was disfranchised for this cause alone. In the early years, registration cost one shilling, and some did not think it worth the price.

The earlier, complicated qualification system, particularly before 1918, facilitated the process by which party political agents maximised the number of their own supporters, and minimised that of their opponents, on the register. The fact that overseers were often party agents facilitated manipulation of the register. Voting preference could be easily judged until the 1872 Ballot Act (35 & 36 V. c.33), by consulting the previous poll book, which indicated how individuals had cast their votes (see our companion Guide to *Poll Books*, Gibson and Rogers, 2008). Since then, it has been achieved largely by house to house enquiries, which continue to this day. The local organisation of political parties, in a sense, grew out of this need and opportunity, as agents indulged in some sharp practices in order to achieve their aims: payment of rates for their poorer supporters, one man's charity being another man's corruption; provision of fictitious receipts for unpaid rents; splitting of freeholds and leaseholds to create spurious ('faggot') voters; and making numerous objections to the inclusion of hostile voters on the register, especially at the last minute, putting victims to the expense of defending their rights – many considered it not worth the cost and dropped off the register. The 1843 Parliamentary Voters Registration Act (6 & 7 V. c.18) tightened this loophole somewhat, but it is nevertheless worth looking at both register and draft (or 'list') if both have survived.

Use of electoral registers

Many genealogists have used the registers as a source of information about addresses in the last century, in order to locate individuals in census returns. The more discerning will also use them for the data they provide on landholding and leases, to find out the year in which individuals reach the age of majority, and to follow the shape of households over time (see Sandison, 1988).

The registers can also be used for studies of surname distribution, and for assessing the scale of geographical mobility (see Grant and Edwards, 1977). Anyone familiar with the problems of locating individuals with whom they have lost contact knows how invaluable they can be (see Rogers, 1986). For those involved in recording oral history, they are a very useful prompting device for memories of people living decades ago in micro-localities.

Presentation and Miscellaneous notes

Libraries holding only copies of current or recent (i.e. post-1948) electoral registers are not included. The absence of other libraries holding earlier material signifies nil returns, but we would be interested to learn of any holdings not appearing in this Guide.

Dates given are the years in which each register came into force. Hence, the six-monthly registers 1918-26, 1945-48 are not normally so distinguished.

No attempt has been made to list the registers held by Electoral Registration Officers, though we have included any which have been notified to us.

Arrangement is by pre-1974 county, and within each county, by **County** constituencies, followed by **Borough** constituencies. Remember that some some earlier Borough consituencies may late be subsumed by County divisions of the same name but different territory; and areas formerly part of County divisions may achieve Borough status at a later date.The only exception to this is Scotland, where the various constituencies and names changes are listed in one alphabetical order. Places are cross-referenced as necessary, especially those Burghs formerly part of 'multiple' Burgh constiuencies.

A major addition to this Guide is the inclusion of full details of the gigantic British Library collection, made possible by the publication of *Parliamentary Constituencies and their registers since 1832* (Cheffins, 1998). This has facilitated the new arrangement by constituency and period of existence. See Youngs (1980, 1991) for the histories of individual constituencies, though these volumes only covers cover England.

Reference numbers have been given only where it is evident that the document concerned is in manuscript form.

Public access to the Guildhall Library is subject to production of evidence of identity. The Society of Genealogists (14 Charterhouse Buildings, Goswell Road, London EC1M 7BA, tel. 020-7702 5480) is open Tuesdays - Saturdays to non-members at a modest hourly or daily charge.

Members of family history societies might note that a number of documents have proved impossible to date by normal means, and should regard this as a challenge to use their skills in order to solve the problem.

The only non-standard abbreviation used is 'AVL', Absent Voters List.

In addition to those listed opposite, references to studies of individual places, using electoral registers as a basis, will be found at the appropriate location in the Guide.

REFERENCES

Note. This list is based on that appearing in the former Guide in 1990. A few recent additions are included, but in no way is it intended to be comprehensive.

T. Abrahams, 'Reading the Rolls' [Electoral Registers], *Ancestors*, **69** (May, 2008).

D. Balsom and I. McAllister, 'Whose vote counts? Electoral registration and the "40 per cent" rule', *Political Quarterly* **51** (1980).

N. Blewett, 'The franchise in the United Kingdom, 1885-1918', *Past and Present* **32** (1965).

E.W. Cox and S.G. Grady, *The New Law and Practice of Registration and Elections* (various editions, 19th century).

H.A. Cheffins, *Parliamentary Constituencies and their registers since 1832* (1998; new edition in preparation). Catalogue of the British Library holdings.

M. Emerson, 'Voting for computers', *Guardian* (25 Jan. 1966).

R. Gant and J.A. Edwards, 'Electoral registers as a resource for geographical enquiry', *Geography* **62** (1977).

J.S.W. Gibson and C.D. Rogers, *Poll Books, c.1695-c.1872: A Directory to holdings in Great Britain*, Fourth edition (2008).

P.G. Gray and E.A. Gee, 'Electoral registration for Parliamentary elections', *Govt. Soc. Survey* **391** (1967).

S. Gray, 'The electoral register', *Govt. Soc. Survey* **M 151** (1970).

Handlist of Pollbooks and Registers of Electors in the Guildhall Library (1970).

N. Holding, *More Sources of World War I Army Ancestry* (1986).

M.N. Jackson, 'Notes on the polling registers in the Public Record Office', *North Cheshire Family Historian* 4.2 (1977).

B. Keith-Lucas, *The English Local Government Franchise* (1952).

M. Pugh, *The Evolution of the British Electoral System 1832-1987* (1988).

M. Rees, 'Defects in the system of electoral registration', *Political Quarterly* **41** (1970).

C.D. Rogers, *Tracing Missing Persons* (1986), s. C15.

F.N. Rogers, *Rogers' on Elections* (various editions, published originally as *The Law and Practice of Elections* in 1820).

A. Sandison, 'Electoral rolls in genealogy', *The Genealogists' Magazine* **22**.10 (June 1988).

A.N. Schofield, *Schofield's Local Government Elections* (various editions from 1949).

C. Seymour, *Electoral Reform in England and Wales* (1915, reprinted 1970).

J.A. Thomas, 'The system of registration and the development of party organisation', *History* **25** (1940).

J.E. Todd and P.A. Dodd, *The Electoral Registration Process in the United Kingdom* (1982).

F.A. Youngs, *Guide to the Local Administrative Units of England* (Vol. 1, Southern England; Vol. 2, Northern England) (1980, 1991). This lists the places or areas in each constituency at different periods.

ACKNOWLEDGMENTS

As with all of my Guides, this could not have been compiled with out the willing assistance of all those archivists and librarians in whose custody these records lie.

Being, in general, printed, but nevertheless surviving in minute quantities, electoral registers occupy that uncertain ground between true manuscript archives and normal published books. Perhaps it is fortunate that, more and more, record offices and local studies libraries are becoming closely linked.

My enquiries, fresh for this Guide, though based on the earlier one, have been met, in most cases, with conscientious and, where necessary, detailed replies. Quite often these have indicated "no change". In others, and Staffordshire comes particularly to mind, the new arrangement by constituencies has revealed confusion or ambiguity that needed expert local knowledge to clarify. It is gratifying now, also, to have a much more comprehensive coverage of the holdings of the National Library of Wales.

A problem for the local expert is that he or she will have such intimate knowledge of the area with which they are dealing that the ignorance of enquirers may be overlooked. Areas with alternative names are an example. Even to those familiar with the registers, the difference between county and borough constituencies can be obscured.

It is my hope that this Guide will shed light on the registers and areas they cover at different times as viewed in a national context. It is also a particular joy to discover unique survivals – usually unsuspected by their custodians. Much work has been put in by countless archivists and librarians to answer my enquiries. This Guide should repay their industry, identifying what is held in a way that no amount of catalogues on-line via "A2A" can provide!

My devout thanks to you all.

J.G.

BEDFORDSHIRE

Abbreviations
BCL = Bedford Central Library.
BL = British Library.
BLA = Bedfordshire & Luton Archives & Record Service, Bedford.
GL = Guildhall Library, London.
SoG = Society of Genealogists.
TNA = The National Archives, Library.

County Constituencies

1832-1885
Bedfordshire. BL 1832-40, 1843-55, 1857, 1859-74, 1876-85; **BLA** 1832-85; **TNA** 1874; **SoG** 1832.

1885-1918
Northern or **Biggleswade Div. BL** 1885/6-90, 1892-1900, 1902-10, 1912-15; **BLA** 1885-1915.
Southern or **Luton Div. BL** 1885/6-90, 1892-1900, 1902-1910, 1912-5; **BLA** 1885-1909, 1912-15.

1918-1948
Bedford Div. BL 1918-31, 1937-38, 1947-48; **BLA** 1918-39, 1945-48.
Luton Div. BL 1918-31, 1937-38, 1947-48; **BLA** 1918-39, 1945-48.
Mid Bedfordshire Div. BL 1918-31, 1947-8; **BLA** 1918-39, 1945-48.

Borough Constituency
Bedford, *1832-1918*. BL 1832, 1834-5, 1839, 1845, 1848-74, 1876-91, 1893-1915; **BLA** 1832 (with MS poll added); Freemen entitled to vote 1914; **GL** 1832-33, 1858.

Burgess Rolls
Bedford. BLA 1747 [R Box 770];
BL East Ward 1843; West Ward 1845.

Some post-1948 ER holdings at *BL* (all), *BLA*, *BCL* and *Luton Central Library.*

BERKSHIRE

Abbreviations
BL = British Library.
BRO = Berkshire Record Office, Reading.
GL = Guildhall Library, London.
RCL = Reading Central Library.
SoG = Society of Genealogists.
TNA = The National Archives, Library.

County Constituencies

1832-1885
Berkshire. BL 1856-65; **TNA** 1874; **GL** 1874; **BRO** 1832 (indexed), 1840-43, 1845, 1848-53, 1855-85; c.1834 (Great Shefford only) [D/P108/1/3A/4]; **RCL** 1832, 1850, 1860; **SoG** 1832, 1838.

1885-1918
Eastern or **Wokingham Div. BL** 1885/6-1915; **BRO** 1886-89, 1894-1902, 1904-15.
Northern or **Abingdon Div. BL** 1885/6-1915; **BRO** 1886-89, 1893-1915.
Southern or **Newbury Div. BL** 1885/6-1915; **BRO** 1886-89, 1894-1901, 1903-15; **RCL** 1887.

1918-1948
Abingdon Div. BL 1919-31, 1837-8, 1947-48; **BRO** 1918-38, 1945-48.
Newbury Div. BL 1919-31, 1937-8, 1947-48; **BRO** 1918-24, 1925 (autumn only), 1926-38, 1945-1948.
Windsor Div. BL 1919-31, 1937-8, 1947-48; **BRO** 1918-1938, 1945-48>.

Borough Constituencies
Abingdon, *1832-85*. BL 1863-6, 1868/9-76; **BRO** 1832, 1866.
New Windsor, *1832-1918*. BL 1853-5, 1857-65, 1868-1873, 1875-83, 1885/6-93, 1896-1902, 1904-5, 1910-5; **BRO** List of voters: 1712; 1853, 1862-3.
Reading, *1832-1948*. BL 1836, 1838-9, 1841-4, 1847, 1853-65, 1895, 1937-8, 1947-8; **BRO** 1835, 1844-51, 1854-1913, 1918-39, 1945-48; **RCL** 1832-41, 1843, 1898, 1910, 1918-1921, 1925-39, 1945, 1947-48.
Wallingford, *1832-85*. BL none; **BRO** 1832-72 (1832 incl. parishes near Wallingford); **TNA** 1874.
Windsor *see* New Windsor.

Burgess Rolls
Newbury. BRO 1836-1914.
Reading. BRO 1848; **RCL** Castle Ward 1835-41, 1843, 1846-1901; Abbey, Castle and Church Wards 1835-63 (gaps).
Wallingford. BRO 1835-52, 1888-1909.

Registers of County Electors
BL 1889-92.

Parochial Registers
Reading. BRO 1894-1914; **RCL** 1894-1901.

Some post-1948 ER holdings at *BL* (all), *BRO, RCL, Bracknell, Maidenhead, Newbury* and *Slough Libraries.*

BUCKINGHAMSHIRE

Abbreviations

BL = British Library.
CBS = Centre for Buckinghamshire Studies, Aylesbury.
GL = Guildhall Library, London.
HWL = High Wycombe Central Library.
TNA = The National Archives, Library.

County Constituencies

1832-1885

Buckinghamshire. BL 1859, 1862, 1885; **TNA** 1874; **HWL** 1834; **GL** 1836; **CBS** 1832-85 (missing 1841/2, 1843/4, 1846/7, 1858/9);

1885-1918

Mid or Aylesbury Div. BL 1885/6-1915; **CBS** 1885/6, 1890.
Northern or Buckingham Div. BL 1885/6-1915; **CBS** 1889-90.
Southern or Wycombe Div. BL 1885/6-1915; **CBS** 1890.

1918-1948

Aylesbury Div.
  BL 1918-9, Spr. 1922-31, 1937-8, 1947-48; **CBS** 1918-39, 1945-8.
Buckingham Div.
  BL 1918-9, Spr. 1921-31, 1937-8, 1947-48; **CBS** 1918-39, 1945-8.
Eton and Slough Div. (1945-8). BL 1947-8; **CBS** 1945-8.
Wycombe Div.
  BL 1918-9, Spr. 1921-31, 1937-8, 1947-48; **CBS** 1918-39, 1945-8; **HWL** ?1931-35.

Borough Constituencies

Aylesbury, 1832-85. BL 1885; **TNA** 1874.
Buckingham, 1832-85. BL 1832-46; **TNA** 1874.
Great Marlow, 1832-85. BL 1843-57, 1859-71, 1885.
Wycombe, Chepping [High], 1832-85.
  BL 1862, 1864, 1871, 1873-85; **TNA** 1875; **HWL** 1832-35[?], 1837-8 *[check]*.

Burgess Rolls

Buckingham. CBS 1835-62, 1866, 1875-84, 1887, 1890-1, 1893, 1898, 1913-15.

Some post-1948 ER holdings at *BL* (all), *CBS, HWL* and *Slough Local History Library*.

CAMBRIDGESHIRE

For Peterborough, see Northamptonshire.

Abbreviations

BL = British Library.
CA = Cambridgeshire Archives, Cambridge.
CCL = Cambridge Central Library.
GL = Guildhall Library, London.
HA = Huntingdonshire Archives, Huntingdon.
TNA = The National Archives, Library.

County Constituencies

1832-1885

Cambridgeshire. BL 1873; Isle of Ely (only) 1875-76; **CA** 1853; Isle of Ely (only) 1832, 1864, 1881; Ely and South Witchford District (only) 1868; **GL** 1842; **TNA** 1872, Isle of Ely (only) 1874.

1885-1918

Eastern or Newmarket Div. BL 1897-1915; **CA** 1913-5; **CCL** 1913, 1915.
Northern or Wisbech Div. BL None; **CA** 1913-5 [?];
Western or Chesterton Div. BL 1897-1915; **CA** 1885, 1913-5 *[?]*; **HA** 1915.

1918-1948

Cambridgeshire. BL 1918-31, 1937-8, 1947-48; **CA** 1926, 1930, 1932, 1935-8, 1945-48; AVL only 1918-20.
Isle of Ely. BL 1937-8, 1947-48; **CA** 1918, 1930, 1932, 1934-9.

Borough Constituency

Cambridge, 1832>. BL 1885/6, 1897, 1901-5, 1908-9, 1911-5, 1921-3, Aut. 1924-31, 1937-8, 1947>; **CA** 1847, 1913-5, 1920-37, 1939; **CCL** 1844-6, 1848-9, 1851-52, 1863, 1868-9, 1871-1874, 1888-89, 1903, 1908-15, 1918-39, 1945>.

University Register

Cambridge.1832-1948. BL 1918-39, 1945-47; **CA** 1925, 1939, 1945.

Burgess Rolls

Cambridge. CA 1842-43, 1850, 1865 (all marked for juries); **CCL** 1849, 1851-52, 1854, 1857-1907. *Published,* Spindrift:1844-5, 1860-61.

Jurors' Books

Cambridgeshire. CA 1828-34, 1847, 1871, 1883.
Isle of Ely. CA 1883, 1899-1922, 1950.

Some post-1948 ER holdings at *BL* (all), *CA, CCL, HA* and *Peterborough Library*.

CHESHIRE

Abbreviations

BCL = Birkenhead Central Library [?Wirral Archives]
BL = British Library.
CCA = Cheshire & Chester Archives & Local Studies, Chester.
GL = Guildhall Library, London.
SCL = Stockport Central Library.
SoG = Society of Genealogists.
TL = Tameside Local Studies Library, Stalybridge.
TNA = The National Archives.
WCL = Warrington Central Library.

County Constituencies

1832-67

Cheshire, Northern Div. *BL* None; *CCA* 1832-52, 1954-6, 1858-60, 1862-3, 1865; *GL* 1834, 1836.
Cheshire, Southern Div. *BL* 1836 (with poll book 1837); *CCA* 1832-52, 1954-6, 1858-60, 1862-3, 1865; *GL* 1834, 1836-40.

1867-85

Mid Cheshire Div. *BL* None; *CCA* 1868, 1870-5; *TNA* 1874. See M.N. Jackson, 'The Mid-Cheshire by-election of 1873', *North Cheshire Family Historian* **4**.3 (1977), incl. surname index for **Lymm**.
North Cheshire Div. *BL* None; *CCA* 1868, 1870-5; *TNA* 1874.
South Cheshire Div. *BL* None; *CCA* 1868, 1870-5; *TNA* 1874.

1885-1918

Altrincham (& Sale) Div. *BL* 1897-1909, 1911-15; *CCA* 1885, 1887-8, 1890-5, 1897-1915; *Sale Library* 1913*[?]*.
Crewe Div. *BL* None; *CCA* 1885, 1887-95, 1897-1915.
Eddisbury Div. *BL* None; *CCA* 1885, 1887-95, 1897-1915.
Hyde Div. *BL* None; *CCA* 1885, 1887-95, 1897-1915; *SCL* 1881*[?]*-92, 1895, 1897-1915; *TL* 1881-92, 1895, 1897-1915; Stalybridge (objections only) 1894.
Knutsford Div. *BL* None; *CCA* 1885, 1887-95, 1897-1915.
Macclesfield Div. *BL* None; *CCA* 1885, 1887-95, 1897-1915.
Northwich Div. *BL* None; *CCA* 1885, 1887-95, 1897-1915.
Wirral Div. *BL* None; *CCA* 1885, 1887-95, 1897-1915; *BCL* 1885, 1887.

1918-48

Altrincham [& Sale?] Div. *BL* 1918-31, 1937-8; *Sale Library* 1935, 1937-9, 1945> [?].
Bucklow Div. (1945-8). *BL* 1947-8; *CCA* 1945-8.
City of Chester Div. *BL* 1918-31, 1937-8, 1947-8; *CCA* 1918-29 (incl. AVL 1919), 1931-9, 1945>.
Crewe Div. *BL* 1918-39, 1947-8; *CCA* 1918-39 (incl. AVL 1919), 1945>.
Eddisbury Div. *BL* 1918-31, 1937-8, 1947-8; *CCA* 1918-39 (incl. AVL 1918-9), 1945-8.

Knutsford Div. *BL* 1918-31, 1937-8, 1947-8; *CCA* 1918-28 (incl. AVL 1919), 19454>.
Macclesfield Div. *BL* 1918-31, 1937-8, 1947-8; *CCA* 1918-28 (incl. AVL 1918-9), 1930-9, 1945>
Northwich Div. *BL* 1918-31, 1937-8, 1947-8; *CCA* 1918-39 (incl. AVL 1919), 1945-74; Runcorn (only) 1939, 1945.
Stalybridge & Hyde Div. *BL* 1918-31, 1937-8, 1947-48; *CCA* 1918-28 (incl AVL 1919), 1930-9, 1945-74; *SCL* 1919-22, 1924-30, 1932-6, 1938, 1945-6; *TL* 1919-22, 1924-30, 1932-36, 1938, 1945-6.
Wirral Div. *BL* 1918-31, 1937-8, 1947-8; *CCA* 1918-39 (incl. AVL 1919), 1945>.

Borough Constituencies

Altrincham & Sale, *1945-70*. *BL* 1947>.
Ashton under Lyne, *1832*> (pt. Dukinfield 1867-1915). *TL* Dukinfield (only) 1895, 1898, 1906, 1919, 1930; objections only 1894, 1906.
Bebington, *1948-70*. *BL* 1949>; *Bebington Reference Library* 1945>.
Birkenhead, *1861-1918*. *BL* 1861-4, 1885/6, 1897; *BCL* 1862-1915.
Birkenhead East Div., *1918-48*. *BL* 1937-8, 1947-8; *BCL* 1918-39, 1945-48.
Birkenhead West Div., *1918-48*. *BL* 1937-8, 1947-8; *BCL* 1918-39, 1945-48.
Chester, *1832-1918*. *BL* 1885/6, 1897; *CCA* 1832, 1836 (MS), 1838, 1840, 1842, 1844-8, 1851-70, 1879-1915.
Macclesfield, *1832-85*. *BL* 1832.
Stalybridge, *1867-1918*. *BL* None. *See also* Ashton under Lyne; Lancs: Hartshead.
Stockport, *1832-1948*. *BL* 1885/6-1915, 1937-8, 1947-8; *SCL* 1834, 1837-9, 1842, 1844-5, 1859, 1865, 1871, 1880-1, 1883-93, 1895, 1906, 1908-14, 1918-39 (incl. AVL 1918-25), 1945-48 (1885-88 indexed); Brinnington only 1871; Heaton Norris (Lancs.) only 1840, 1859, 1871, 1920-39; township 1905-15; parish 1918-9; Reddish North (Lancs.) only 1935.
Wallasey, *1918*>. *BL* 1937-8, 1947>; *CCA* 1914 [?]; *BCL* 1907-15, 1918-39, 1945>.
Warrington (in Lancashire from 1918), *1832*>. *BL* 1859-66, 1868/9-72, 1875-6, 1879-80, 1885/6, 1937-8, 1947>; *WCL* 1832-1914, 1918-21, 1924-39, 1945> (incl. revisions 1874-94, 1899).

Burgess Rolls

Chester. *CCA* c.1835-6, 1840-1, 1846-67, 1869-74, 1876-78.
Stockport. *SCL* 1483 (copy), 1832, 1835-41, 1843-6, 1849-53, 1855-65, 1867, 1869-71, 1874, 1876 (name index only, 1885-88); *SoG* 1835.
Warrington. *WCL* 1847-80 (except 1866).

County Council Registers

County. *CCA* 1890-1915 (with district gaps).

Cheshire continued on page 18.

17

Cheshire continued

Freeholders/Freemen/Jurymen
County. *CCA* 1578 (published, ed. W.F. Irvine,
Lancashire & Cheshire Record Society **43**, 1902).
Chester. *CCA* 1392-1805 (pubd, ed. J.H.E. Bennett,
Lancashire & Cheshire R.S. **51**, **55**, 1906, 1908).
Stockport, Heaton Norris. *SCL* 1872-3, 1875-6,
1879, 1906-12, 1913-21[sic], objection 1886.
Warrington. *WCL* 1885-94, 1897-9, 1901-14.

Parochial Registers
Altrincham. *CCA* 1894, 1896-1915.
Crewe. *CCA* 1894, 1896-1915.
Hyde. *CCA* 1894, 1896-1915.
Knutsford. *CCA* 1894, 1896-1915.
Macclesfield. *CCA* 1894, 1896-1915.
Northwich. *CCA* 1894, 1896-1915.

Post-1948 ER holdings at *BL, BCL, CCA, SCL, TL,
WCL, Lancashire Record Office, Preston* and
*Bebington, Crewe, Ellesmere Port, Macclesfield,
Manchester Central, Sale* and *Wilmslow Libraries.*

CORNWALL
Abbreviations
BL   = British Library.
CLS = Cornwall Local Studies Library, Redruth.
CRO = Cornwall Record Office, Truro.
GL   = Guildhall Library, London.
TNA = The National Archives.

County Constituencies
1832-85
Cornwall, Eastern Div. *BL* None; *GL* 1837;
CLS 1858-9, 1865-8; *TNA* 1874.
Cornwall, Western Div. *BL* None; *TNA* 1874;
CLS 1858-9, 1865-8.

1885-1918
Mid or **St Austell Div.** *BL* 1885/6, 1897, 1906.
North Eastern or **Launceston Div.** *BL* 1885/6, 1897,
1906.
North Western or **Camborne Div.** *BL* 1885/6, 1897,
1906.
South Eastern or **Bodmin Div.** *BL* 1885/6, 1897,
1906.
(South) Western or **St Ives Div.** *BL* 1885/6, 1897,
1906.
Truro Div, *BL* 1885/6, 1897, 1906.

1918-48
Bodmin Div. *BL* 1922-Spr. 1923, 1924-31, 1937-8,
1947-8; *CRO* 1924-39, 1945>.
Camborne Div. *BL* Aut. 1922-31, 1937-8, 1947-8;
CRO 1922-39, 1945-6.
Northern Div. *BL* Aut. 1922-31, 1937-8, 1947-8;
CRO 1922-39, 1945>.
Penryn & Falmouth Div. *BL* Aut. 1922-Spr. 1926,
1927-31, 1937-8, 1947-8; *CRO* 1922-39, 1945-8.
St Ives Div. *BL* Aut. 1922-31, 1937-8, 1947-8;
CRO 1922-39, 1945>.

Cornwall continued

Borough Constituencies
Bodmin, *1832-85.* *BL* 1832, 1834-63; *TNA* 1874.
Helston, *1832-85.* *BL* 1863; *TNA* 1875.
Launceston, *1832-5.* *BL* 1859-63; *TNA* 1872.
Liskeard, *1832-85.* *BL* None; *TNA* 1873.
Penrhyn & Falmouth, *1832-1915.* *BL* 1842, 1848,
1853, 1856, 1861-73, 1875, 1878-87, 1889-1905,
1907-9, 1914-5.
St Ives, *1832-85.* *BL* 1850-5, 1857, 1859-63, 1870,
1872-3, 1882-4; *TNA* 1875.
Truro, *1832-85.* *BL* None.

Post-1948 ER holdings at *BL, CLS, CRO* and
Plymouth Central Library.

CUMBERLAND
Now part of Cumbria
Abbreviations
BL   = British Library.
BRO = Cumbria Record Office, Barrow-in-Furness.
CL   = Carlisle Library.
CRO = Cumbria Record Office, Carlisle.
TNA = The National Archives.
WRO = Cumbria Record Office, Whitehaven.

County Constituencies
1832-85
Cumberland, Eastern Div. *BL* None; *CRO* 1833-5,
1838-9, 1841, 1843-5, 1847-51, 1853-9, 1861-2,
1864-5, 1868, 1870, 1874-5; *CL* 1837; *TNA* 1874;
University of Durham 1874 (Cumrew (pt) and
Warwick Bridge polling districts only, annotated with
canvass results [H.N.C.586/bundle 1].
Cumberland, Western Div. *BL* None;
CRO 1832-3, 1835-6, 1839, 1841-7, 1849, 1851,
1854-9, 1861-5, 1867-8, 1870, 1873-75; *TNA* 1874;
WRO 1832-33, 1835, 1839-75 (incomplete);
BRO c.1878-85 (incomplete coverage,
Waberthwaite, Ulpha, Millom and area).

1885-1918
Mid or **Penrith Div.** *BL* 1905-15; *CRO* 1899-1914.
Northern or **Eskdale Div.** *BL* 1905-15;
CRO 1885, 1892, 1895, 1899-1900, 1902-15.
Southern or **Cockermouth Div.** *BL* 1905-15;
CRO 1899-1914; *WRO* 1899-1914..
Western or **Egremont Div.** *BL* 1905-15;
CRO 1899-1915; *BRO* c.1885-1915 (incomplete
coverage, Waberthwaite, Ulpha, Millom and area),
1894-5 (north); *WRO* 1899-1915.

1918-48
Northern Div. *BL* 1937-8, 1947-8;
CRO 1918-39, 1945-8.
Penrith & Cockermouth Div. *BL* 1937-8, 1947-8;
CRO 1918-39, 1945>; *WRO* 1918-39, 1945-48.
Whitehaven Div. *BL* 1937-8, 1947-8;
CRO 1918-39, 1945>; *BRO* 1924 (Haverigg South,
Holborn Hill, Newton North and South (Millom) only),
1918 (Whicham only); *WRO* 1918-39, 1945>;
Workington Div. *BL* 1937-8, 1947-8;
CRO 1918-39, 1946>; *WRO* 1918-39, 1946>.

Cumberland continued

Borough Constituencies
Carlisle, *1832*>. *BL* 1841-65, 1871-1901, 1920-31, 1937-8, 1947>; *CRO* 1832-42, 1865-8, 1870-91, 1893-1915, 1919, 1924-6, 1929-30, 1932-3, 1938-39, 1945, 1947-49; *CL* 1894-1915, 1918-39, 1945>; *TNA* 1875 (incl. freemen).
Cockermouth, *1832-85*. *BL* None; *TNA* 1874.
Whitehaven, *1832-85*. *BL* 1841, 1847, 1851, 1853, 1858, 1864, 1866-72, 1874, 1885; *TNA* 1875.

Burgess Rolls
Carlisle. *CRO* 1835-1912, 1914.

Parochial Registers
Carlisle. *CRO* 1895-1904, 1906-12, 1915.

County Council electors
Carlisle. *CRO* 1891, 1893-1913.

Post-1948 ER holdings at *BL, CL, CRO* and *WRO*.

DERBYSHIRE

Abbreviations
BL = British Library.
CL = Chesterfield Library.
DL = Derby Library.
DRO = Derbyshire Record Office, Matlock.
GL = Guildhall Library, London.
LSL = Derbyshire Local Studies Library, Matlock.
SoG = Society of Genealogists.
TNA = The National Archives.

County Constituencies
1832-67
Derbyshire, Northern Div. *BL* None; *DRO* 1832-67; *LSL* 1832, 1836, 1838, 1840-2, 1844-6; *CL* 1832, 1836, 1838, 1840, 1845-6; *DL* 1836, 1840, 1842; *GL* 1832 (with poll added).
Derbyshire, Southern Div. *BL* None; *DRO* 1832-67; *LSL* 1832, 1835, 1837-9, 1841-2, 1844-5, 1847; *DL* 1832, 1837-9, 1842, 1844, 1857; *SoG* 1832; *GL* 1832 (with poll added).

1867-85
East Derbyshire Div. *BL* None; *DRO* 1868-84; *TNA* 1868, 1870.
North Derbyshire Div. *BL* None; *DRO* 1868-84; *TNA* 1870.
South Derbyshire Div. *BL* None; *DRO* 1868-84; *TNA* 1870.

Derbyshire continued

1885-1918
Chesterfield Div. *BL* None; *DRO* 1885-1915.
High Peak Div. *BL* None; *DRO* 1885-1915.
Ilkeston Div. *BL* None; *DRO* 1885-1915.
Mid Derbyshire Div. *BL* None; *DRO* 1885-1915.
North Eastern Derbyshire Div. *BL* None; *DRO* 1885-1915.
Southern Derbyshire Div. *BL* None; *DRO* 1885-1915.
Western Derbyshire Div. *BL* None; *DRO* 1885-1915.

1918-48
Belper Div. *BL* 1937-8, 1947-8; *DRO* 1918-39, 1945-1948.
Chesterfield Div. *BL* 1937-8, 1947-8; *DRO* 1918-39, 1945-8; *CL* 1925-8, 1930-9, 1945>.
Clay Cross Div. *BL* 1937-8, 1947-8; *DRO* 1918-39, 1945-8.
High Peak Div. *BL* 1937-8, 1947-8; *DRO* 1918-39, 1945-8; *Glossop Library* 1933 (Glossop only).
Ilkeston Div. *BL* 1937-8, 1947-8; *DRO* 1918-39, 1945-8; *Buxton Library* 1946-8 (Buxton only).
North Eastern Derbyshire Div. *BL* 1937-8, 1947-8; *DRO* 1918-39, 1945-8.
Southern Derbyshire Div. *BL* 1937-8, 1947-8; *DRO* 1918-39, 1945-8.
Western Derbyshire Div. *BL* 1937-8, 1947-8; *DRO* 1918-39, 1945-8.

Borough Constituency
Derby, *1832-1948*. *BL* 1897-1915, 1918-31, 1937-8, 1947-8; *DL* 1834, 1836, another (n.d.), 1844-51, 1853, 1855-6, 1858-70, 1872, 1874, 1876-7, 1879-1880, 1883-4, 1886-94, 1896-1909, 1912-5, 1918-1939, 1945>; *SoG* 1835 (Derby South).

Burgess Rolls
Chesterfield. *CL* 1835-1914 (gaps).
Derby. *DL* 1862-9, 1871-90, 1893-4, 1901-2, 1904-5, 1907-11, 1913-4; *BL* 1832, 1836.
Glossop. *Glossop Library* 1897, 1908.

Freeholders
Melbourne. *DRO* 1789 [D.655 A/PO 945].

Parochial Registers
Duffield. *DL* 1894.

Post-1948 ER holdings at *BL, CL, DL, DRO* and *Buxton, Glossop, Ilkeston, Swadlincote* and *Manchester Central Libraries.*

DEVON

Devon *continued*

Abbreviations
BL = British Library.
DRO = Devon Record Office, Exeter (see their leaflet "Electoral Registers").
NDR = North Devon Record Office, Barnstaple.
PCL = Plymouth Central Library.
SoG = Society of Genealogists.
TCL = Torquay Central Library.
TNA = The National Archives.
WCS = West Country Studies Library, Exeter Central Library.

County Constituencies

1832-67

Devonshire, Northern Div. *BL* 1862-67; *DRO* 1832, 1836, 1838, 1839, 1841-1867 (gaps covered by overseers' lists); *WCS* 1839; *NDR* 1832-67.
Devonshire, Southern Div. *BL* 1862-67; *DRO* 1832, 1836, 1839, 1841-67 (gaps covered by overseers' lists); *NDR* 1832-67.

1867-85

East Devonshire Div. *BL* 1868-75; *DRO* 1868-85; *NDR* 1868-85; *TNA* 1874.
North Devonshire Div. *BL* 1868-75; *DRO* 1868-85; *NDR* 1868-85; *TNA* 1874.
South Devonshire Div. *BL* 1868-75; *DRO* 1868-85; *NDR* 1868-85; *TNA* 1874.

1885-1918

Eastern or **Honiton Div.** *BL* 1885/6-91, 1893-5, 1897, 1899-1908, 1910-5; *DRO* 1885-1915; *NDR* 1885-95.
Mid or **Ashburton Div.** *BL* 1885/6-91, 1893-5, 1897, 1899-1908, 1910-5; *DRO* 1885-1915; *NDR* 1885-1895.
North Eastern or **Tiverton Div.** *BL* 1885/6-91, 1893-1895, 1897, 1899-1908, 1910-5; *DRO* 1885-1915; *NDR* 1885-95.
North Western or **Barnstaple Div.** *BL* 1885/6-91, 1893-1895, 1897, 1899-1908, 1910-5; *DRO* 1885-1915; *NDR* 1885-95.
Northern or **South Molton Div.** *BL* 1885/6-91, 1893-1895, 1897, 1899-1908, 1910-5; *DRO* 1885-1915; *NDR* 1885-95.
Southern or **Totnes Div.** *BL* 1885/6-91, 1893-1895, 1897, 1899-1908, 1910-5; *DRO* 1885-1915.
Torquay Div. *BL* 1885/6-91, 1893-1895, 1897, 1899-1908, 1910-5; *DRO* 1885-1915; *NDR* 1885-95.
Western or **Tavistock Div.** *BL* 1885/6-91, 1893-95, 1897, 1899-1908, 1910-5; *DRO* 1885-1915; *NDR* 1885-95.

1918-48

Barnstaple Div. *BL* 1918-31, 1937-8, 1947-8.
Honiton Div. *BL* 1919-31, 1937-8, 1947-8.
South Molton Div. *BL* 1919-31, 1937-8, 1947-8.
Tavistock Div. *BL* 1918-31, 1937-8, 1947-8.
Tiverton Div. *BL* 1918-31, 1937-8, 1947-8.
Torquay Div. *BL* 1918-31, 1937-8, 1947-8 *TCL* 1936-9, 1945>.
Totnes Div. *BL* 1918-31, 1937-8, 1947-8.

Borough Constituencies

Ashburton, *1832-1918*. BL None.
Barnstaple, *1832-85*. BL None; *NDR* 1832-64 (gaps); *TNA* 1875.
Dartmouth, *1832-1918*. BL 1859-63.
Devonport, *1832-1918*. BL 1885/6, 1897; *PCL* 1885-1886.
Exeter, *1832>*. BL 1885/6-87, 1898-1915, 1920-31, 1937-8, 1947>; *DRO* 1843>; *WCS* 1932-9, 1945>; *University of Manchester Library* 1864. *SoG* 1859;
Honiton, *1832-67*. BL None; *WCS* 1839.
Plymouth, *1832-1918*. BL 1885/6.
Plymouth Devonport Div., *1918>*. BL 1937-8, 1947>; *PCL* 1934-9, 1945-6.
Plymouth Drake Div., *1918-48*. BL 1937-8, 1947-8; *PCL* 1934-9, 1945-6.
Plymouth Sutton Div., *1918>*. BL 1937-8, 1947>; *PCL* 1935-7, 1945-6.
Plymouth Crownhill. *PCL* 1945-6.
Tavistock, *1832-85*. BL None.
Tiverton, *1832-85*. BL None; *TNA* 1875.
Totnes, *1832-1918*. BL None.

Burgess Rolls

Barnstaple. *NDR* 1639, 1674-5, 1729, 1758, 1774-1831 (incomplete), 1835, 1852, 1854-5.
Great Torrington. *NDR* 1835-53.
Torquay. *TCL* 1912.

Freemen

Barnstaple. *NDR* 1832-49, 1853, 1855, 1882-5.

Post-1948 ER holdings at *BL, DRO, WCS, NDR, PCL, TCL, Westcountry Studies Library, Exeter* and *West Devon Record Office, Plymouth.*

DORSET

Abbreviations
BL = British Library.
DHC = Dorset History Centre, Dorchester.
PCL = Poole Central Reference Library.
SoG = Society of Genealogists.
TNA = The National Archives.
WL = Weymouth Reference Library.
WM = Weymouth Local History Museum.

County Constituencies

1832-85

Dorsetshire. BL 1859-85; *DHC* 1833-85; *PCL* 1883 (Eastern only); *TNA* 1874; *SoG* 1838.

Dorset: *County Constituencies* continued

1885-1918
Eastern Div. *BL* 1885/6-90, 1892-1915;
DHC 1885-1915; *PCL* 1885-6 (incl. Poole).
Northern Div. *BL* 1885/6-90, 1892-1915;
DHC 1885-1915
Southern Div. *BL* 1885/6-90, 1892-1915;
DHC 1885-1915
Western Div. *BL* 1885/6-90, 1892-1915;
DHC 1885-1915

1918-48
Eastern Div. *BL* 1918-31, 1937-8, 1947-8;
DHC 1918-39, 1945>; *PCL* 1932-3 (Poole only).
Northern Div. *BL* 1918-31, 1937-8, 1947-8;
DHC 1918-39, 1945>
Southern Div. *BL* 1918-31, 1937-8, 1947-8;
DHC 1918-39, 1945>; *WM* 1930-9 (Weymouth
only); *WL* 1932, 1937 (both Broadway only), 1946>
(Weymouth only).
Western Div. *BL* 1918-31, 1937-8, 1947-8;
DHC 1918-39, 1945>

Borough Constituencies
Bridport, *1832-67. BL* 1863;
DHC 1832-8, 1840-42, 1855, 1857, 1859-60, 1864-
1868, 1870-4, 1877-8, 1881-84.
Dorchester, *1832-85. BL* 1851, 1854, 1858-75,
1878-1881; *DHC* 1843-8, 1855-68, 1875-7.
Lyme Regis, *1832-85. BL* None.
Poole, *1832-85. BL* 1850, 1852, 1854, 1856-9, 1861-
1875, 1877-85; *PCL* 1846, 1865, 1882; *TNA* 1871.
Shaftesbury, *1832-85. BL* 1854; *DHC* 1883;
TNA 1873.
Wareham, *1832-85. BL* 1842-5, 1848-51, 1853-8,
1860-3; *TNA* 1872.
Weymouth & Melcombe Regis, *1832-85. BL* None;
WL 1834, 1837.

Burgess Rolls
Bridport. *DHC* 1882, 1886-88.
Blandford Forum. *DHC* 1887.
Corfe Castle. *DHC* 1780 [D.1/JF 1].
Dorchester. *DHC* 1835-69, 1885-7, 1890-1, 1895,
1900.
Lyme Regis. *DHC* 1835-91.
Poole. *PCL* 1761, 1830 (copy), 1866, 1868.

Post-1948 ER holdings at *BL, DHC, PCL, WL* and
Ferndown (Wimborne) Library; also *Bournemouth
(Lansdowne)* and *Christchurch Libraries* and
Hampshire Record Office for places formerly in
Hampshire.

County DURHAM

Abbreviations
BL	=	British Library.
DL	=	Darlington Library (has an excellent collection of local political material).
DRO	=	Durham County Record Office (list of parishes, showing Parliamentary divisions, available).
DUL	=	Durham University Library, Archives and Special Collections.
GCL	=	Gateshead Central Library.
GL	=	Guildhall Library, London.
NCL	=	Newcastle upon Tyne Central Library.
NCS	=	Northumberland Collections Service, Ashington.
SCL	=	Sunderland Central Library.
SoG	=	Society of Genealogists.
SRL	=	Stockton Reference Library.
SSL	=	South Shields Central Library.
TNA	=	The National Archives.

Tyne & Wear Archive Service issues a leaflet (User
Guide 17) listing microfilm held of ERs, mainly for
1835-6 only, by place (in Newcastle area?), so
actual constituency or even county cannot be
identified.

County Constituencies

1832-85
Co. Durham, Northern Div. *BL* 1868/9; *DRO* 1832-
1885; *DL* 1868; *NCS* 1868-9 (with poll added);
NCL 1832, 1868; *SoG* 1868; *GL* 1853; 1868 (with
poll added; *TNA* 1874 (Pt 1 only); *University of
Manchester Library* 1868 (with poll added).
Co. Durham, Southern Div. *BL* 1868/9;
DRO 1832-1885; *DL* 1833, 1855, 1860-2, 1865,
1868; 1874 (Cockerton only);
NCS 1868-9 (with poll added);
Middlesbrough Library 1869-78 (Billingham only);
NCL 1832, 1868; *GL* 1868 (with poll added);
TNA 1874 (Pt 2 only).

1885-1918
Barnard Castle Div. *BL* 1885/6-1915;
DRO 1885-1915.
Bishop Auckland Div. *BL* 1885/6-1915;
DRO 1885-1915; *DL* 1913.
Chester-le-Street Div. *BL* 1885/6-1915;
DRO 1885-1915.
Houghton-le-Spring Div. *BL* 1885/6-1915;
DRO 1885-1915.
Jarrow Div. *BL* 1885/6-1915;
DRO 1885-1915.
Mid Div. *BL* 1885/6-1915; *DRO* 1885-1915.
North Western Div. *BL* 1885/6-1915;
DRO 1885-1915.
South Eastern Div. *BL* 1885/6-1915;
DRO 1885-1915; *DL* 1890.

Co. Durham: *County Constituencies* continued

1918-48

Barnard Castle Div. *BL* 1918-31, 1937-8, 1947-8; *DRO* 1918-38, 1945>.

Bishop Auckland Div. *BL* 1918-31, 1937-8, 1947-8; *DRO* 1918-38, 1945>.

Blaydon Div. *BL* 1918-31, 1937-8, 1947-8; *DRO* 1918-38, 1945>.

Chester-le-Street Div. *BL* 1918-31, 1937-8, 1947-8; *DRO* 1918-38, 1945>.

Consett Div. *BL* 1918-31, 1937-8, 1947-8; *DRO* 1918-38, 1945>.

Durham Div. *BL* 1918-31, 1937-8, 1947-8; *DRO* 1918-38, 1945>.

Houghton-le-Spring Div. *BL* 1918-31, 1937-8, 1947-1948; *DRO* 1918-38, 1945>.

Jarrow Div. *BL* 1918-31, 1937-8, 1947-8; *DRO* 1918-38, 1945>.

Seaham Div. *BL* 1918-31, 1937-8, 1947-8; *DRO* 1918-38, 1945>.

Sedgefield Div. *BL* 1918-31, 1937-8, 1947-8; *DRO* 1918-38, 1945>.

Spennymoor Div. *BL* 1918-31, 1937-8, 1947-8; *DRO* 1918-38, 1945>.

Borough Constituencies

Darlington, *1867>. *BL* 1885/6, 1897, 1899, 1937-8, 1947>; *DL(DRO)* 1868 (draft); *DL* 1868-70, 1874, 1884-1902, 1904-14, 1918-39, 1945>.

Durham, *1832-1918. *BL* 1852, 1897-9, 1901-2, 1914-1915; *DL* 1870 (poll result added); *NCL* 1871; *SoG* 1870 (with 1871 poll); *GL* 1868 (with poll added).

Gateshead, *1832-1948. *BL* 1885/6-1915, 1918-31, 1937-8, 1947-8; *GCL* 1832, 1837, 1842, 1847, 1851, 1918-39, 1945>.

The Hartlepools, *1868-1970. *BL* 1885/6-1913, 1915, 1918-31, 1937-8, 1947-70; *TNA* 1874.

Morpeth (N'hmbd.) incl. Bedlington (co. Durham until 1844) – see under Northumberland.

South Shields, *1832>. *BL* 1937-8, 1947>; *SSL* 1850-1915, 1918-39, 1945>; *Tyne & Wear Archives Service, Newcastle upon Tyne* 1848.

Stockton-on-Tees, *1867-1970. *BL* 1885/6, 1889-1915, 1937-8, 1947-70; *SRL* 1926, 1939, 1945; *TNA* 1875.

Sunderland, *1832-1948. *BL* 1885/6, 1937-8, 1947-8; *DUL* 1885 (Tunstall, Ryhope polling district, incomplete); *SCL* 1841-2, 1849-50, 1853, 1857-8, 1862, 1868, 1870, 1873-4, 1885, 1891, 1895-1914, 1918, 1920, 1922, 1924-5, 1928, 1930-38.[some may be burgess rolls]; *SoG* 1834 (p'copy).

Lists of Freeholders

Chester, Darlington, Easington, Stockton Wards. *DL(DRO)* 1783; *DL* 1793.

Burgess Rolls

Bishopwearmouth. *SCL* 1850 [or ER].

Darlington. *DL* 1868 (draft).

Gateshead. *GCL* 1835-6, 1840, 1847, 1862-4, 1867-1870, 1872-3, 1875-91, 1894-8, 1900-4, 1906-14.

Monkwearmouth. *SCL* 1842, 1844-45 [ER?].

South Shields. *SSL* 1850-1915, 1918-39, 1945>.

Sunderland. *SCL* – see left.

Post-1948 ER holdings at *BL, DL, DRO, GCL, NCL, SCL, SRL, SSL* and *Middlesbrough Central Library.*

ESSEX

Abbreviations

BL = British Library.
CL = Colchester Central Library.
ERO = Essex Record Office, Chelmsford.
GCL = Grays Central Library.
GL = Guildhall Library,London.
SRL = Stratford Reference Library (Newham LS).
TNA = The National Archives.
VHM = Vestry House Museum (LB of Waltham Forest LS Section), Walthamstow.
Note. Holdings formerly at Essex R.O. Colchester or Southend are now at E.R.O. Chelmsford.

County Constituencies

1832-67

Essex, Northern Div. *BL* 1841, 1863-7; *ERO* 1832-3, 1835-8, 1843-58, 1861, 1863-67 (some incomplete).

Essex, Southern Div. *BL* 1859, 1863-7; *ERO* 1832-67 (missing 1840, 1860); *GCL* Little Thurrock only, 1840; *Southend Central Library* 1833; *SRL* East Ham, West Ham (Stratford, Church Street, and Plaistow wards), Little Ilford 1832-1867 (Mf); *VHM* Leyton only 1845, Walthamstow only 1856-7, 1860-5.

1867-85

North-East Essex Div. *BL* 1869-75, 1885; *ERO* 1869-1885; *TNA* 1875.

North-West Essex Div. *BL* 1869-75, 1885; *ERO* 1869-1870, 1872-85; *TNA* 1875.

South Essex Div. *BL* 1869-75, 1885; *ERO* 1869-85; *TNA* 1875; *SRL* (Mf as above), 1867-89[?]; *VHM* Walthamstow only 1867-70, 1874-5.

1885-1918

Eastern or Maldon Div. *BL* 1885/6-1915; *ERO* 1899-1915.

Mid or Chelmsford Div. *BL* 1885/6-1915; *ERO* 1886-1915.

Northern or Saffron Waldon Div. *BL* 1885/6-1915; *ERO* 1889-1915.

North-Eastern or Harwich Div. *BL* 1885/6-1915; *ERO* 1886-1915.

Southern or Romford Div. *BL* 1885/6-1915; *ERO* 1889-1915; *SRL* 1885-1915, 1918 (Mf, East Ham and Little Ilford only).

South-Eastern Div. *BL* 1885/6-1915; *ERO* 1886-1915.

Essex: *County, 1885-1918* continued

South-Western or **Walhamstow Div.** *BL* 1885/6-1915; *ERO* 1886-1915;
VHM Leyton 1893-7, Cann Hall 1893-6, Leyton & Cann Hall 1897-1915, Walthamstow 1906-15, 1918.
Western or **Epping Div.** *BL* 1885/6-1915;
ERO 1889-1915.

1918-48
Chelmsford Div. *BL* 1918-31, 1937-8, 1947-8;
ERO 1918-39, 1945-8.
Colchester Div. *BL* 1918-31, 1937-8, 1947-8;
ERO 1918-39, 1945-8; *CL* 1918-26, 1928-30 (AVL's for 1918-25, 1927-8), 1936-9, 1945-6.
Epping Div. *BL* 1918-31, 1937-8, 1947-8;
ERO 1918-1939, 1945-8;
VHM Chingford 1939, 1947.
Harwich Div. *BL* 1918-31, 1937-8, 1947-8;
ERO 1918-1939, 1945-8.
Hornchurch Div. *(1945-48)*. *BL* 1947-8; *ERO* 1945-8.
Maldon Div. *BL* 1918-31, 1937-8, 1947-8;
ERO 1918-1939, 1945-8.
Romford Div. *BL* 1918-Aut. 1923, Aut. 1924-31, 1937-1938, 1947-8; *ERO* 1918-39, 1945-8;
Havering Central Library Romford 1939.
Saffron Walden Div. *BL* 1918-31, 1937-8, 1947-8;
ERO 1918-39, 1945-8.
South-Eastern Div. *BL* 1918-31, 1937-8, 1947-8;
ERO 1918-39, 1945-8;
GCL (Thurrock only): 1936-8, 1948 (civilians only).
Thurrock Div. *(1945-48)*. *BL* 1947-8; *ERO* 1945-8.

Borough Constituencies
Barking, *1945-70. BL* 1947>.
Colchester, *1832-1918. BL* 1846-50, 1852-5, 1857-8, 1860-3, 1879-89, 1895-1915;
ERO 1840, 1846, 1852; 1875-1904 (incl. burgesses listed separately); *CL* 1832, 1835-36, 1873-75, 1886-92, 1894-7, 1900-14; *TNA* 1874.
Dagenham, *1945-70. BL* 1947>.
East Ham, North Div., *1918-70. BL* 1937-8, 1947>;
SRL 1919-39, 1945>.
East Ham, South Div., *1918-70. BL* 1937-8, 1947>;
SRL 1919-39, 1945>.
West Ham, North Div., *1885-1918. BL* None;
SRL 1890-1915, 1918.
West Ham South Div., *1885-1918. BL* None;
SRL 1890-1915, 1918.
West Ham, Plaistow Div., *1918-48. BL* 1937-1948; *SRL* 1919-39, 1945-8.
West Ham, Silvertown Div., *1918-48. BL* 1937-8, 1947-8; *SRL* 1919-39, 1945-8.
West Ham, Stratford Div., *1918-48. BL* 1937-1948; *SRL* 1919-39, 1945-8.
West Ham, Upton Div, *1918-48. BL* 1937-8, 1947-8; *SRL* 1919-39, 1945-8.
Harwich, *1832-85. BL* None.
Ilford, *1918-45. BL* 1937-8.
Ilford, North Div., *1945-70. BL* 1947>.
Ilford, South Div., *1945-70. BL*. 1947>.
Leyton, East Div., *1918-48. BL* 1937-8, 1947-8.
Leyton, West Div., *1918-48. BL* 1937-8, 1947-8.

Maldon, *1832-85. BL* 1832; *ERO* 1836 (incomplete; with note of 1837 poll); *GCL* 1832.
Romford, *1945-70. BL* 1947>.
Southend-on-Sea, *1918-48. BL* 1937-8, 1947-8.
Walthamstow, East Div., *1918-70. BL* 1937-8, 1947>; *VHM* 1918, 1921, 1932-6, 1946>.
Walthamstow, West Div., *1918-70. BL* 1937-8, 1947>; *VHM* 1918, 1921, 1932-6, 1946>.
Woodford, *1945-64. BL* 1947>.

Burgess Rolls
Colchester. *ERO* 1818, 1835-78 [MS, Acc C1], 1848-9, 1852, 1854, 1859, 1862-3, 1867; 1871, 1875-97;
CL 1887-9, 1891, 1893-4; *GL* 1835, 1858.
Maldon. *ERO* 1911.

Freemen
Maldon. *ERO* 1844, 1851.

Parochial Registers
Colchester. *CL* 1895, 1897.

Post-1948 ER holdings at *BL, CL, ERO, GCL, SRL, VHM* and *Brentwood, Harlow, Havering (Romford)* and *Southend Libraries.*

GLOUCESTERSHIRE and BRISTOL

Abbreviations
BCL = Bristol Central Library.
BL = British Library.
BRO = Bristol Record Office.
GA = Gloucestershire Archives, Gloucester (Gloucester Library now at Glos. Archives.
GL = Guildhall Library, London.
SoG = Society of Genealogists.
TNA = The National Archives.

Publication. *Index to Gloucestershire ERs 1831/2,* Microfiche, Glos. FHS.

County Constituencies

1832-85
Gloucestershire, Eastern Div. *BL* None; *GA* 1832-1882 (except 1833, 1861), also 1833-50 (MS), Stow district only 1854 [D.1395/1/13]; *GRL* 1832-85;
GL 1843; *TNA* 1874. Facsimile 1832 published on CD by BBC *Who Do You Think You Are?*, Feb 2008.
Gloucestershire, Western Div. *BL* None; *GA* 1832-1885, also 1833-50 (MS); *SoG* 1832, 1837;
GL 1853; *TNA* 1874. Facsimile 1832 published on CD by BBC *Who Do You Think You Are?*, Feb 2008.

1885-1918
Eastern or **Cirencester Div.** *BL* 1885/6, 1897;
GA 1885-1915.
Forest of Dean Div. *BL* 1885/6, 1897;
GA 1885-1915.
Mid or **Stroud Div.** *BL* 1885/6, 1897; *GA* 1885-1915.
Northern or **Tewkesbury Div.** *BL* 1885/6, 1897;
GA 1885-1915.
Southern or **Thornbury Div.** *BL* 1885/6, 1897;
GA 1885-1915; *BCL* Westbury-on-Trym only 1914.

Gloucestershire: *County* continued

1918-1948
Cirencester & Tewkesbury Div. *BL* 1937-8, 1947-8;
  GA 1918-39, 1945>.
Forest of Dean Div. *BL* 1937-8, 1947-8;
  GA 1918-1939, 1945>.
Stroud Div. *BL* 1937-8, 1947-8; *GA* 1918-39, 1945>;
Thornbury Div. *BL* 1937-8, 1947-8;
  GA 1918-39, 1945>.

Borough Constituencies
Bristol, *1832-85. BL* 1832, 1864, 1866-84;
  BRO 1832, 1834, 1843-78, 1880,1882-85;
  BCL 1832, 1834-85 [or 1834, 1836, 1864, 1868,
  1870-75]; *TNA* 1874;
  University of Manchester Library 1832.
Bristol, East (Div.), *1885-1948. BL* 1937-8, 1947-8;
  BRO 1885-1915, 1918-39, 1945>;
  BCL 1885-1913 [or 1895 only].
Bristol, Central (Div.), *1918-70. BL* 1937-8, 1947-70;
  BRO 1918-39, 1945>;
Bristol, North (Div.), *1885-1948. BL* 1937-8, 1947-8;
  BRO 1885-1915, 1918-39, 1945>;
  BCL 1885-1913 [or 1895 only].
Bristol, South (Div.), *1885>. BL* 1937-8, 1947>;
  BRO 1885-1915, 1918-39, 1945>;
  BCL 1885-1913 [or 1895 only].
Bristol, West (Div.), *1885>. BL* 1937-8, 1947>;
  BRO 1885-1915, 1918-39, 1945>; *BCL* 1885-1913
  [or 1895 only].
Cheltenham, *1832>. BL* 1853-7, 1859-63, 1870,
  1897-1915, 1918-31, 1937-8, 1947>;
  BCL 1885-1913 [or 1895 only];
  Cheltenham Library 1892-1915, 1918-39, 1945>.
Cirencester, *1832-85. BL* 1849, 1851-3, 1856-7,
  1860-1864; *GA* 1841 [D.674a X4]; *TNA* 1872;
  Bingham Library Cirencester 1848-69 [also 1802?].
Gloucester, *1832>. BL* 1868/9-70, 1874, 1876-9,
  1883, 1885/6-1902, 1904-5, 1907-15, 1918-31,
  1937-8, 1947>; *GA* 832-1915, 1918-39, 1945>.
  Facsimile 1832 published on CD by BBC *Who Do
  You Think You Are?*, Feb 2008.
Stroud, *1832-85. BL* 1863-4; *TNA* 1873
Tewkesbury, *1832-85. BL* None; *TNA* 1874.

Burgess Rolls
Bristol. *BRO* 1557-99, 1607-1726, 1728-date (all MS
  [04358-9]); 1882-1915.

Freeholders and Freeman
Bristol. *SoG* 1722.

Ward Lists
Bristol. *BRO* 1835-52.

Post-1948 ER holdings at *BL, BCL, BRO, GA* and
Cheltenham Library.

HAMPSHIRE
Abbreviations
BL   = British Library.
GL   = Guildhall Library, London.
HRO = Hampshire Record Office, Winchester.
IWR = Isle of Wight Record Office, Newport.
LLB = Lansdowne Reference Library,
         Bournemouth.
PRS = Portsmouth Records Service.
SAS = Southampton Archives Service.
SCL = Southampton City Library.
SoG = Society of Genealogists.
TNA = The National Archives.

County Constituencies
1832-85
Hampshire, Northern Div. *BL* None; *SoG* 1836;
  TNA 1874.
Hampshire, Southern Div. *BL* None; *GL* 1834;
  TNA 1874.
Isle of Wight. *BL* 1866;
  IWR n.d. (*c.*1843), 1848, 1850, 1852.

1885-1918
Eastern or Petersfield Div. *BL* 1897-1915;
  HRO 1896-1900, 1904, 1906-8, 1913-4.
New Forest Div. *BL* 1897-1915;
  HRO 1893, 1897-1900, 1902, 1904-7, 1913, 1915.
Northern or Basingstoke Div. *BL* 1897-1915;
  HRO 1899, 1902, 1904, 1906-7, 1913-4.
Southern or Fareham Div. *BL* 1897-1915;
  HRO 1896-1899, 1901, 1904-8, 1915.
Western or Andover Div. *BL* 1897-1915;
  HRO 1896-98, 1900, 1902, 1904, 1906-7, 1911,
  1913-4.
Isle of Wight. *BL* None.

1918-48
Aldershot Div. *BL* 1918-21, 1923-31, 1937-8, 1947-8;
  HRO 1918-28, 1930-9, 1945>.
Basingstoke Div. *BL* 1918-21, 1923-31, 1937-8,
  1947-8; *HRO* 1918-39, 1945>.
Fareham Div. *BL* 1918-21, 1923-31, 1937-8, 1947-8;
  HRO 1918-28, 1930-9, 1945-48.
New Forest & Christchurch Div. *BL* 1918-21, 1923-
  1931, 1937-8, 1947-8;
  HRO 1918-28, 1930-9; 1945>.
Petersfield Div. *BL* 1918-21, 1923-31, 1937-8, 1947-
  1948; *HRO* 1918-28, 1930-9, 1945>.
Winchester Div. *BL* 1918-21, 1923-31, 1937-8, 1947-
  1948; *HRO* 1918-28, 1930-9, 1945>.
Isle of Wight. *BL* 1937-8,1947>.

Borough Constituencies
Andover, *1832-85. BL* None; *TNA* 1874.
Bournemouth, *1918-48. BL* 1918-31, 1937-8, 1947-8;
  LLB 1919-399, 1945, 1947>.
Christchurch, *1832-1918. BL* 1854, 1864-6, 1868/9-
  1874, 1876-9, 1885-7, 1892-1902, 1904-5, 1907-8,
  1913-5.
Lymington, *1832-85. BL* None.

Hampshire: *Boroughs* continued

Newport (IoW), *1832-85.* **BL** 1859-66;
IWR 1832, 1841, 1843, 1848.
Petersfield, *1832-85.* **BL** 1850-63; *TNA* 1874;
Somerset Archive & Record Service 1832-3.
Portsmouth, *1832-1918.* **BL** 1854;
PRS 1832-64 (also MS 1832-43), 1877, 1879-1914.
Portsmouth, Central Div., *1918-48.* **BL** 1937-8, 1947-1948; *PRS* 1918-39, 1945>.
Portsmouth, North Div., *1918-48.* **BL** 1937-8, 1947-48; *PRS* 1918-39, 1945>.
Portsmouth, South Div., *1918>.* **BL** 1937-8, 1947>;
PRS 1918-39, 1945>.
Southampton, *1832-1948.* **BL** 1854, 1860, 1885/6-1902, 1937-8, 1947-8; *SAS* 1832-1915, 1918, 1930-1939, 1945>; register of proxies 1918-9, 1921-39;
SCL 1832-9, 1845-8, 1851-1915, 1918-39, 1945>.
National Archives of Scotland [sic] 1846
[GD364/1/518].
Winchester, *1832-1918.* **BL** 1843-63, 1885/6.

Burgess Rolls
Andover. *HRO* 1853, 1884 [37M85 11/PE/46-47].
Bournemouth. *LLB* 1890-1909, 1911-2, 1918.
Portsmouth. *PRS* (MS): 1835-46, 1849-52; 1853 (St.
Thomas Ward only); 1876; (printed): 1835, 1838-65,
1867-9, 1872-78.
Southampton. *SAS* 1835-75 (earlier volumes being
MS), 1877-1915; burgess admissions: 1496-1835.

Freemen/Freeholders
Southampton. *SAS* freemen admissions: 1614-1726;
lists of freeholders: 1793, 1798, 1826, 1833.

Winchester. *HRO* 1833, 1835, 1838, 1840-1 (all MS);
1838, 1841-57, 1859-62, 1866, 1868-9, 1878, 1880,
1885, 1888, 1893, 1900, 1907-1915 [W/B9/1/1-43].

Parochial Registers
Abbots Ann to Yately. *HRO* 1896.

Post-1948 ER holdings at *BL, HRO, IWR, LLB,
PRS, SAS, SCL* and *Christchurch Library.*

HRO has 'Various places (Aldershot to Wickham)
1889-90, 1892-95; (Kingsclere to Wickham) 1891;
Aldershot to South Liberty 1896-7.'

HEREFORDSHIRE

See M.C. Dunn and K. Swindell, 'Electoral registers
and rural migration: a case study from Herefordshire',
Area **14** (1972).

Abbreviations
BL = British Library.
BRL = Birmingham Reference Library, Local
Studies.
HRO = Herefordshire Record Office, Hereford.
TNA = The National Archives.

County Constituencies
1832-85
Herefordshire. *BL* 1842-9, 1851-77, 1879-85;
HRO 1832-3, 1835, 1840 (part), 1843 (part), 1849,
1850, 1853 (part), 1859, 1860 (part), 1863 (part),
1868 (part), 1870, 1880, 1883 (part);
BRL 1874-8, 1880, 1885; *TNA* 1874.

1885-1918
Northern or **Leominster Div.** *BL* 1885/6-7;
HRO 1892, 1900, 1904, 1906, 1910, 1914 [1902-1913?].
Southern or **Ross Div.** *BL* 1885/6-92, 1897;
HRO 1892, 1900, 1904, 1906, 1910, 1914.

1918-48
Hereford Div. *BL* Aut. 1919-Spr. 1923, Spr. 1924,
Spr. 1925-28, 1930-1, 1937-8, 1947-8;
HRO 1918-39, 1945>.
Leominster Div. *BL* Aut. 1919-Spr. 1923, Spr. 1924,
Spr. 1925-28, 1930-1, 1937-8, 1947-8;
HRO 1918-1939, 1945>.

Borough Constituencies
Hereford, *1832-1918.* **BL** 1860-5, 1868, 1897-1915.
Leominster, *1832-85.* **BL** None; *HRO* 1839, 1843.
Ludlow, 1832-85. *BL* None.

Post-1948 ER holdings at *BL* and *HRO.*

HERTFORDSHIRE

Abbreviations
BL = British Library.
GL = Guildhall Library, London.
HA = Hertfordshire Archives & Local Studies, Hertford.
SAL = St Albans Central Library.
SoG = Society of Genealogists.
TNA = The National Archives.
WCL = Watford Central Library.

County Constituencies

1832-85
Hertfordshire. *BL* 1860; *HA* 1832-43 (MS); 1842, 1844-56, 1858-62, 1865-85, draft lists 1832-85 (incl. names removed in final version); *SAL* 1874; *WCL* 1832, 1845 (copy); *SoG* 1832 (with poll added); *GL* 1832 (with poll added); *TNA* 1875.

1885-1918
Eastern or **Hertford Div.** *BL* 1885/6, 1897-1915; *HA* 1895-1915; draft lists 1885-93;
Cheshunt Library Cheshunt only 1886, 1888, 1894.
Mid or **St Albans Div.** *BL* 1897-1915; *HA* 1895-1915; draft lists 1885-93.
Northern or **Hitchin Div.** *BL* 1885/6, 1897-1915; *HA* 1895-1915; draft lists 1885-93; *SAL* 1906.
Western or **Watford Div.** *BL* 1885/6, 1897-1915; *HA* 1895-1915; draft lists 1885-93.

1918-1948
Barnet Div. (1945-48). *BL* 1947-8.
Hemel Hempstead Div. *BL* 1919-30, 1937-8, 1947-8; *HA* 1918-22, 1924-30, 1932; incl. AVL 1918-22, 1924-8, 1930-1.
Hertford Div. *BL* 1919-30, 1937-8, 1947-8; *HA* 1918-1922, 1924-6, 1928; incl. AVL 1918-22, 1924-8, 1930-1931; *Cheshunt Library* Cheshunt only 1938, 1945.
Hitchin Div. *BL* 1919-30, 1937-8, 1947-8; *HA* 1918-1922, 1924-30, 1932; incl. AVL 1918-22, 1924-8, 1930-1.
St Albans Div. *BL* 1919-30, 1937-8, 1947-8; *HA* 1918-1922, 1924-30, 1932; incl. AVL 1918-22, 1924-8, 1930-1.
Watford Div. *BL* 1919-30, 1937-8, 1947-8; *HA* 1918-1922, 1924-30, 1932; incl. AVL 1918-22, 1924-8, 1930-1.

Borough Constituencies
Hertford, 1832-85. *BL* None; *HA* 1832, 1843-8, 1851, 1856, 1861, 1868-9, 1871-1873, 1875-84, 1918-39, 1945>.
St Albans, 1832-52. *BL* None.

Burgess Rolls
Hertford. *HA* 1885-6, 1888, 1890, 1892, 1894-5, 1897, 1911-3.

Post-1948 ER holdings at *BL, HA, Cheshunt, Hatfield, Hertford, Hitchin, Hoddesdon, Letchworth, St Albans, Watford* and *Welwyn Garden City Libraries*.

HUNTINGDONSHIRE
Now part of Cambridgeshire.

See Dr. P. Saunders, "Huntingdonshire Poll Books and Electoral Registers to 1900', *Hunts FHS Journal*, 1989.
G. Proby's burgess lists in *Trans. Cambs. & Hunts. Arch. Soc.* **5**.
VCH Huntingdonshire ii, 22-61 'Political History'.

Abbreviations
BL = British Library.
CA = Cambridgeshire Archives, Cambridge.
HA = Huntingdonshire Archives, Huntingdon.
NM = Norris Museum, St Ives.
TNA = The National Archives.

County Constituencies

1832-85
Huntingdonshire. *BL* 1860-3; *HA* 1834-6; *c.*1838 (Toseland Hundred only); 1842 (copy); 1844; 1865 (returns and draft only); *NM* 1834, 1836, 1839; *TNA* 1874.

1885-1918
Northern or **Ramsey Div.** *BL* None.
Southern or **Huntingdon Div.** *BL* None.

1918-1983
Huntingdonshire. *BL* 1937-8, 1947>; *HA* 1920, 1928-33, 1935-7, 1939, 1946.

Borough Constituency
Huntingdon, 1832-85. *BL* 1857-63; *HA* 1832; 1837-1843 (some MS); 1851, 1856-7; 1870 (unfit for consultation); *TNA* 1874.

Burgess Rolls
Huntingdon. *HA* 1765, 1768, 1770, 1773, 1776, 1779, 1782, 1784-7; 1794 (residents only); 1802, 1806-7; 1809 (residents only); 1812; 1818 (draft); 1825 (residents only); 1826; others, post-1832.

Jury Book
Huntingdonshire. *CA (Cambridge)* 1883.

Post-1948 ER holdings at *BL, HA, Electoral Registration Office, Huntingdonshire District Council, Huntingdon* and *Peterborough Central Library*.

KENT

See W.F. Bergess and B.R. Riddell, *Kent Directories Located*, 2nd ed. (1978).

Abbreviations

BCL = Bromley Central Library.
BL = British Library.
BxL = Bexley Local History Library.
CCL = Canterbury Central Library.
CKS = Centre for Kentish Studies, Maidstone.
GL = Guildhall Library, London.
GCL = Gravesend Central Library.
MAS = Medway Archives & Local Studies Centre, Strood.
RGM = Guildhall Museum, Rochester.
SoG = Society of Genealogists.
TNA = The National Archives.

County Constituencies

1832-67

Kent, Eastern Div. *BL* 1850-67; *CKS* 1832-38; 1840 (incomplete); 1863 1865-8; also 1832-65 (MS) [Q/RPr/2/1-66]; claims and objections 1832-78 (MS) [Q/RPr 4/1,2]; Norton parish only 1845 [U.419/.2]; *Margate Central Lib* Margate St John parish only 1850.

Kent, Western Div. *BL* 1850-67; *CKS* 1832-38; 1840 (incomplete); 1855-7, 1859-63, 1865-8; also 1832-65 (MS) [Q/RPr/2/1-66]; claims and objections 1832-78 (MS) [Q/RPr 4/1,2]; Tenterden only 1836 (property owners) [Te/AE.3]; Maidstone property owners: 1835-7, 1839, 1841-1842, 1853, 1859-60; Maidstone voters: 1850, 1859; objections: 1839, 1841, 1846, 1851; Sutton Valence property owners 1844. *GCL* objections: Gravesend 1848; Northfleet 1847, 1853;

1867-85

Kent: Eastern Div. *BL* 1867-85; *CKS* 1870-85; *TNA* 1874.

West Kent: Mid Kent Div. *BL* 1868/9-85; *TNA* 1874. *CKS* 1868, 1870-85; Tonbridge only c.1867-77 (annotated re. votes cast) [U.55/011/1-6]; 1875-6, 1879; 1881 (draft); 1882, 1885; objections 1881-2;

West Kent: West Kent Div. *BL* 1868/9-85; *CKS* 1868, 1870-85; *ML* Maidstone voters 1875-6, 1879, 1885; *TNA* 1874.

1885-1918

Eastern or St Augustine's Div. *BL* 1885/6-1907; *CKS* 1886-9, 1901-04, 1908-15.

Mid or Medway Div. *BL* 1885/6-1907; *CKS* 1886-9, 1901-15.

North Eastern or Faversham Div. *BL* 1885/6-1907; *CKS* 1886-89, 1901-15.

North Western or Dartford Div. *BL* 1885/6-1907; *CKS* 1886-89, 1901-07, 1909-15; objections 1905 (part). 1915 (claimants); Maidstone voters 1910; *BxL* 1906-15 (Erith).

Southern or Ashford Div. *BL* 1885/6-1907; *CKS* 1886-9, 1901-06, 1908-15.

Isle of Thanet Div. *BL* 1885/6-1907; *CKS* 1886-9,1901-11, 1913-15.

South Western or Tonbridge (Tunbridge) Div. *BL* 1885/6-1907; *CKS* 1886-9.

Western or Sevenoaks Div. *BL* 1885/6-1907; *CKS* 1886-9, 1901-15; *Sevenoaks Lib* 1912-4; *BCL* 1912-5.

1918-48
(§ = incl. AVL register for 1918)

Ashford Div. *BL* 1937-8, 1947-8; *CKS* 1918§-39, 1945>

Canterbury Div. *BL* 1918-Spr. 1921, 1937-8, 1947-8; *CKS* 1918§-20, 1922-39, 1945>; *CCL* 1937-9, 1947>.

Chislehurst Div. *BL* 1937-8, 1947-8; *BCL* 1918-27, 1934-9; Orpington only 1938; *BxL* 1935, 1938, 1945>; *CKS* 1918§-39, 1945>.

Dartford Div. *BL* 1937-8, 1947-8; *BxL* 1937-9, 1945; Erith only 1919, 1926-7, 1929-36, 1939, 1945-8; *CKS* 1918§-39, 1945>.

Dover Div. *BL* 1937-8, 1947-8; *CKS* 1918§-39, 1945>; *Dover Lib* 1924, 1934-5, 1937-8, 1946>; *Deal Lib* 1924.

Faversham Div. *BL* 1937-8, 1947-8; *CKS* 1918§-39, 1945>.

Gravesend Div. *BL* 1937-8, 1947-8; *CKS* 1918§-39, 1945>;.*GCL* 1919, 1923-1926, 1928, 1933, 1935-7, 1939; 1945 (incl. Rural area, and Services list); 1945>.

Isle of Thanet Div. *BL* 1937-8, 1947-8; *CKS* 1918§-1939, 1945>; *Margate Central Lib* Margate only 1926-30, 1932, 1934, 1936, 1938-9, 1947>.

Maidstone Div. *BL* 1918-21, 1930-1, 1937-8, 1947-8; *CKS* 1918§-39, 1945.

Orpington Div. *(1945-8).* *BL* 1947-8; *CKS* 1945>.

Sevenoaks Div. *BL* 1937-8, 1947-8; *CKS* 1918§-39, 1945>; *Sevenoaks Lib* 1918-38, 1945>.

Tonbridge Div. *BL* 1937-8, 1947-8; *CKS* 1918§-39, 1945>.

Borough Constituencies

Bexley, *1945-70.* *BL* 1947-70; *BxL* 1945-70; *CKS* 1945>.

Bromley, *1918-70.* *BL* 1937-8, 1947-70; *CKS* 1945>; *BCL* 1918 (incl. Beckenham and Penge); 1925-6, 1929-30, 1932-3, 1937, 1939, 1945>; Beckenham only 1918, 1925-6, 1929-30, 1932, 1939, 1946>; Penge only 1918, 1925-6, 1929-30, 1932, 1939.

Canterbury, *1832-1918.* *BL* 1854-5, 1857-63, 1885/6-1915; *CCL* 1848-1914,; *TNA* 1873.

Chatham, *1832-1918.* *BL* 1854, 1887-91, 1897, 1899, 1901-3.

Dartford, *1945-55.* *BL* 1947>; *Dartford Central Lib* 1946>.

Deptford, *1885-1918.* *BL* 1885/6, 1888-91, 1897. After 1918, see under London.

Dover, *1832-1918.* *BL* 1897.

Gravesend, *1867-1918.* *BL* 1898; *MAS* 1865-81 (Strood rural parishes); *GCL* 1869 (Milton only); 1897, 1902, 1904, 1907-10, 1912-3, objections 1848; Northfleet. 1893.

Kent: *Borough Constituencies* continued

Greenwich, *1832-1918* (post-1918 see under
London). *BL* 1874-85, 1900; *GL* 1856, 1858;
Greenwich LH Lib 1837, 1845, 1868, 1870-1, 1875,
1892-4, 1898; 1899 (occupiers); 1900; 1901-5
(occupiers); 1906, 1908, 1910-2, 1915.

Hythe, *1832-1948*. *BL* 1844-54, 1857, 1893, 1895-
1902, 1904, 1906-15; Aut. 1921-31, 1937-8, 1947-8;
CKS 1918§-39, 1945-48.

Lewisham – *see under* London.

Maidstone, *1832-1918*.
1832 published on microfiche by Kent FHS.
BL 1841-75, 1885/6-88, 1892-1895, 1897, 1900,
1907-15; *CKS* 1832-68, 1870-6, 1878-80, 1882-
1904, 1907-8, 1911, 1913-4; 1909; objections 1839,
1841, 1846, 1851, 1875-6, 1879, 1885; 1905 (part);
property owners: 1835-9, 1841, 1844, 1846-7, 1851-
1855, 1859-1861, 1868, 1870-3, 1875, 1877-9;
SoG 1845, 1851, 1856, 1861, 1883, 1901, 1913.

Rochester, *1832-1918*. *BL* None; *RGM* 1859-1915.

Rochester, Chatham Div., *1918-48*. *BL* 1937-8,
1947-1948; *MAS* 1931, 1934-9, 1945-6;
RGM 1918-39, 1945> (some gaps); *CKS* 1933-37,
1939, 1945-48.

Rochester, Gillingham Div., *1918-48*. *BL* 1937-8,
1947-48; *MAS* 1931, 1934-1939, 1945-6; *RGM*
1918-39, 1945> (some gaps).

Sandwich (incl. Deal, Walmer), *1832-85*. *BL* 1849-
1885; *CKS* 1832-9, 1844-1885; *Deal Lib* 1832 (MS);
SoG 1831-1836.

Woolwich, *1885-1918* (post-1918 see under London).
BL None; *Greenwich LH Lib* 1900-14; *BxL* Erith only
1905-15.

Burgess Rolls

Bromley. *BCL* 1905-13.

Canterbury. *CCL* 1837 (Northgate Ward).

Chatham. *MAS* 1903-13.

Deal. *CKS* North Ward 1860-1913 [B De/RB.1]; South
Ward 1862-87, 1899-1902, 1910-11 [B De/RB.2-5];

Faversham. *CKS* 1835-83, 1895-96.

Folkestone. *CKS* 1835-50, 1867, 1875-77 [RP.1/1-7].

Chalk. *GCL* 1839.

Cobham. *GCL* 1841, 1845-9.

Denton. *GCL* 1842, 1844.

Gravesend. *GCL* 1839, 1841-51.

Maidstone. *CKS* 1835, 1838-70 (from 1880 with
Parliamentary register), 1890-1914 (incl. objections
in 1906); burgesses (Maidstone parish): 1859, 1878;
claimants/objections: 1839, 1851, 1868, 1879, 1881;
TNA 1865; *SoG* 1869.

Margate. *Margate Central Lib* 1857, 1858 (part),
1873 (Fort Ward only), 1911-4.

Milton. *GCL* 1839, 1841, 1847.

Northfleet. *GCL*. 1844-53.

Queenborough. *CKS* 1715, 1754, 1761, 1766, 1768,
1774, 1780, 1783, 1802, 1817 [Qb/RP.1].

Rochester. *RGM* 1892-95, 1911.

Sandwich. *CKS* 1843-83, 1886-7.

Freeholders' lists incl. out-count/Freemen

County. *CKS*. 1733, 1742, 1753, n.d. (MS) [U.269/0
108 and 113]; 1781 [U.1475/0 159]; 1818 [U.1453/0
88/13].

Canterbury. *CCL* 1392-1800 (pub'd, ed. J.M. Cowper,
1903); 1832-34; *GL* 1392-1800.

Deal. *CKS* 1699-1834 and 1800-35 [B De/RF.1,2].

Maidstone. *CKS* freemen admissions: 1600-17
[Md/Rr/1/1], 1694-1754 [Rf.1/1], 1723-4 [Rf.1/4],
1734-87 [Rf.1/2], 1788-1837 [Rf.1/3]; admissions
1598-1721 [Rf.2/1]; objections 1701-1838 [Rf.1/5].

Sandwich. *CKS* freemen: *c.*1761, 1764, 1768, *c.*1769,
1770-90, *c.*1800-13, 1830; freemen admissions:
1761-96; freemen petitioners: 1718-1821.

Jury qualified

Denton. *GCL* 1842.

Gravesend. *GCL* 1842-5.

Maidstone. *CKS* Jury lists: 1838-50, 1860, 1870, 1872,
1879-81, 1883-6, 1891, 1893-5, 1898, 1906-13, 1920-1.

Northfleet. *GCL*. 1843, 1845-52.

Post-1948 ER holdings at *BL*, CKS, *Ashford,
Broadstairs, Canterbury, Chatham, Dartford, Deal,
Dover, Gillingham, Gravesend, Maidstone, Margate,
Rochester, Sevenoaks, Tunbridge Wells Libraries*
and *Guildhall Museum, Rochester.*

LANCASHIRE

List of Freeholders in Lancashire in 1600, ed. J.P.
Earwaker, Record Society of Lancashire and Cheshire
12 (1875).

Abbreviations

BL	=	British Library.
GL	=	Guildhall Library, London.
LL	=	Brown, Hornby & Picton Libraries, Liverpool.
LRO	=	Lancashire Record Office, Preston.
MCL	=	Manchester Central Library.
SLH	=	Salford Local History Library.
SoG	=	Society of Genealogists.
TLS	=	Tameside Local Studies Library, Stalybridge.
TNA	=	The National Archives.
WCL	=	Warrington Central Library.
WRO	=	Wigan Record Office, Leigh.

County Constituencies

1832-67

Lancashire, Northern Div. *BL* 1863-7;
LRO 1832-60, 1866; *Blackburn Central Lib* 1832;
Lancaster Central Lib 1834-7; *MCL* 1865;
University of Manchester 1832; *GL* 1835.

Lancashire, Southern Div. *BL* 1863-7;
LRO 1832-61, 1866; *Blackburn Central Lib* 1832;
Bury Lib 1832-6 (copy: Ainsworth, Pilkington,
Pilsworth, Prestwich, Radcliffe only), 1846
(Prestwich only); *MCL* 1832, 1840, 1853-4, 1865;
Salford Hundred 1835; *University of Manchester*
1832; *TLS* 1857 'Stalybridge Lancashire Ward';
Wigan RO 1836-7, Atherton only 1845;
GL 1836 (Salford Hundred only).

Lancashire: *County* continued

1867-85

North Lancashire, North-East Div. *BL* 1868-85;
LRO 1870, 1875, 1880, 1885; *TNA* 1874.
Accrington Lib Accrington only 1878-9, 1881;
North Lancashire, North Div. *BL* 1868-85;
LRO 1870, 1875, 1880, 1885;
Barrow Lib 1882-5 (Barrow only); *TNA* 1874.
South Lancashire, South-East Div. *BL* 1868-85;
LRO 1870, 1875, 1880, 1885; *TNA* 1874;
Bury & *Radcliffe Libs* 1883 Radcliffe only;
South Lancashire, South-West Div. *BL* 1868-85;
LRO 1870, 1875, 1880, 1885; *TNA* 1874;.*St Helens
Community Leisure Dept* 1874-85 St Helens only,
with burgess rolls), 1880 (St Helens only);
Wigan RO 1876 (Ince-in-Makerfield only).

1885-1918

Accrington Div. (N.E. Lancs.) *BL* 1885/6, 1887-1915;
LRO 1885-6, 1889-90, 1894, 1900, 1905, 1910;
Accrington Lib 1887-1900, 1902-14.
Blackpool Div. (N. Lancs.) *BL* 1885/6-1915;
LRO 1885-6, 1889-90, 1894, 1900-1, 1905-6, 1910.
Bootle Div. (S.W. Lancs.) *BL* 1885/6-1915;
LRO 1885-1886, 1889-90, 1894, 1900, 1905, 1910.
Chorley Div. (N. Lancs.) *BL* 1885/6-1915;
LRO 1885-1886, 1889-90, 1894, 1900, 1905, 1910.
Clitheroe Div. (N.E. Lancs.) *BL* 1885/6-1915;
LRO 1885-6, 1889-90, 1900, 1905, 1910.
Darwen Div. (N.E. Lancs.) *BL* 1885/6-1915;
LRO 1885-6, 1889-90, 1894, 1900, 1905, 1910.
Eccles Div. (S.E. Lancs.) *BL* 1885/6-1915;
LRO 1885-1886, 1889-90, 1894, 1900, 1905, 1910.
Gorton Div. (S.E. Lancs.) *BL* 1885/6-1915;
LRO 1885-1886, 1889-90, 1894, 1900, 1905, 1910.
Heywood Div. (S.E. Lancs.) *BL* 1885/6-1915;
LRO 1885-6, 1889-90, 1894, 1900, 1905, 1910.
Ince Div. (S.W. Lancs.) *BL* 1885/6-1915;
LRO 1885-6, 1889-90, 1894, 1900, 1905, 1910.
Lancaster Div. (N. Lancs.) *BL* 1885/6-1915;
LRO 1885-6, 1889-90, 1894, 1900, 1905, 1910.
Leigh Div. (S.W. Lancs.) *BL* 1885/6-1915;
LRO 1885-1886, 1889-90, 1894, 1900, 1905, 1910;
Leigh Lib 1890-1914 [?if Leigh only or all Leigh Div.].
North Lonsdale Div. (N. Lancs.) BL 1885/6-1915;
LRO 1885-6, 1889-90, 1894, 1900, 1905, 1910;
Cumbria RO: Barrow 1906, 1910 (both incomplete);
Broughton in Furness area 1895-1915 (incomplete).
Middleton Div. (S.E. Lancs.) *BL* 1885/6-1915;
LRO 1885-6, 1889-90, 1894, 1900, 1905, 1910.
Newton Div. (S.W. Lancs.) *BL* 1885/6-1915;
LRO 1885-6, 1889-90, 1894, 1900, 1905, 1910;
Wigan RO 1906-7 (Ashton in Makerfield only).
Ormskirk Div. (S.W. Lancs.) *BL* 1885/6-1915;
LRO 1885-6, 1889-90, 1894, 1900, 1905, 1910.
Prestwich Div. (S.E. Lancs.) *BL* 1885/6-1915;
LRO 1885-6, 1889-90, 1894, 1900, 1905, 1910, 1914.
Radcliffe cum Farnworth Div. (S.E. Lancs.)
BL 1885/6-1915;
LRO 1885-6, 1889-90, 1894, 1900, 1905, 1910;
Bury & *Radcliffe Libs* 1912 Radcliffe only.

Rossendale Div. (N.E. Lancs.) *BL* 1885/6-1915;
LRO 1885-6, 1889-90, 1894, 1900, 1905, 1910;
Rawtenstall only 1891-1915; *Rawtenstall Lib* 1897-
1915 Rawtenstall only.
Southport Div. (S.W. Lancs.) *BL* 1885/6-1915;
LRO 1885-1886, 1889-90, 1894, 1900, 1905, 1910.
Stretford Div. (S.E. Lancs.) *BL* 1885/6-1915;
LRO 1885-1886, 1889-90, 1894, 1900, 1905, 1910;
Stretford Lib 1890.
Westhoughton Div. (S.E. Lancs.) *BL* 1885/6-1915;
LRO 1885-6, 1889-90, 1894, 1900, 1905, 1910.
Widnes Div. (S.W. Lancs.) *BL* 1885/6-1915;
LRO 1885-6, 1889-90, 1894, 1900, 1905, 1910.

1918-48

Chorley Div. BL Aut. 1921-31, 1937-8, 1947-8;
LRO 1934, 1939, 1945-6 (incl. servicemen).
Clitheroe Div. *BL* Aut. 1921-31, 1937-8, 1947-8;
LRO 1934, 1939, 1945 (incl. servicemen), 1946
(servicemen only).
Darwen Div. *BL* Aut. 1921-31, 1937-8, 1947-8;
LRO 1934, 1939, 1945-6 (incl. servicemen).
Farnworth Div. *BL* Aut. 1921-31, 1937-8, 1947-8;
LRO 1934, 1939, 1945-6 (incl. servicemen);
Bury Lib Ainsworth only 1933.
Fylde Div. *BL* Aut. 1921-31, 1937-8, 1947-8;
LRO 1934, 1939, 1945-6 (incl. servicemen).
Heywood & **Radcliffe Div.** *BL* Aut. 1921-31, 1937-8,
1947-8; *LRO* 1934, 1939, 1945-6 (incl. servicemen);
Bury & *Radcliffe Libs* 1939, 1945 ?Radcliffe only;
Heywood Lib 1927, 1929-33, 1935-40 (sic, incl.
service voters 1940); 1945>-.
Ince Div. *BL* Aut. 1921-31, 1937-8, 1947-8;
LRO 1934, 1939, 1945-6 (incl. servicemen).
Lancaster Div. *BL* Aut. 1921-31, 1937-8, 1947-8;
LRO 1934, 1939, 1945-6 (incl. servicemen).
Lonsdale Div. *BL* Aut. 1921-31, 1937-8, 1947-8;
LRO 1934, 1939, 1945; *Cumbria RO Barrow:* 1921-
1929, 1931-38.
Middleton & **Prestwich Div.** *BL* Aut. 1921-31, 1937-
38, 1947-8; *LRO* 1934, 1939, 1945-6 (incl.
servicemen); *Middleton Central Lib* 1922, 1925-6,
1929-32, 1948; Middleton only 1945-7.
Mossley Div. *BL* Aut. 1921-31, 1937-8, 1947-8;
LRO 1934, 1939, 1945-6 (incl. servicemen);
Oldham LS & *Archives* 1937-8 Failsworth only.
Newton Div. *BL* Aut. 1921-31, 1937-8, 1947-8;
LRO 1934, 1939, 1945-6 (incl. servicemen);
TLS 1939 (Winwick only).
Ormskirk Div. *BL* Aut. 1921-31, 1937-8, 1947-8;
LRO 1934, 1939, 1945-6 (incl. servicemen).
Royton Div. *BL* Aut. 1921-31, 1937-8, 1947-8;
LRO 1934, 1939, 1945-6 (incl. servicemen).
Stretford Div. *BL* Aut. 1921-31, 1937-8, 1947-8;
LRO 1934, 1939, 1945-6 (incl. servicemen);
Stretford Lib 1933 (pt.), 1938.
Waterloo Div. *BL* Aut. 1921-31, 1937-8, 1947-8;
LRO 1934, 1939, 1945-6 (incl. servicemen).
Westhoughton Div. *BL* Aut. 1921-31, 1937-8, 1947-8;
LRO 1934, 1939, 1945-6 (incl. servicemen).
Widnes Div. *BL* Aut. 1921-31, 1937-8, 1947-8;
LRO 1934, 1939, 1945-6 (incl. servicemen);.

Lancashire continued

Borough Constituencies

Accrington, *1918>*. BL 1927, 1937-8, 1947-83; *Accrington Lib* 1920-1, 1930-5, 1937-9, 1945-8; with Church, Clayton le Moors, Oswaldtwistle and Rishton, 1918-9 (both incl. AVL), 1922-9, 1936.

Ashton-under-Lyne, *1832>*. BL 1885/6-7, 1897, 1937-1938, 1947>; *TLS* 1836, 1847 (part), 1848, 1851, 1862, 1897-1915; 1918-9 (incomplete); 1925 (Waterloo only); 1931-39; 1915 (Audenshaw only).

Barrow in Furness, *1885>*. BL 1885/6-1902, 1904-1915, 1918-31, 1937-8, 1947>; *Barrow Lib* 1885-1915, 1918-39, 1945>.

Blackburn, *1832-1948*. BL 1859-63, 1885/6, 1897-1915, Aut. 1921-31, 1937-8, 1947-8; *Blackburn Central Lib* 1832, 1835, 1841-68; also 1868 (MS, annotated with intentions and voting); 1870, 1872, 1874, 1876-1882, 1884-1914, 1918-29, 1931, 1934, 1939, 1945>.

Blackpool, *1918-45*. BL Aut. 1921-Spr. 1922, 1923-1931, 1937-8.

Bolton, *1832-1948*. BL 1857-1900, 1902-5, 1907-15, 1918-31, 1937; *Bolton Ref Lib* 1868-1913, 1926-39, 1945>.

Bootle, *1918>*. BL 1937-8, 1947>.

Burnley, *1867>*. BL 1897, 1899, 1937-8, 1947>; *Burnley Lib* 1891-1905, 1910, 1912-4; 1918-9 (AVL only); 1920-39, 1946>.

Bury, *1832-1948*. BL 1861-3, 1885/6-89, 1897-1902, 1937-8, 1947-8; *Bury Lib* 1836, 1877-81, 1883, 1885, 1888-92, 1894-1915, 1926, 1929-39, 1945.

Clitheroe, *1832-85*. BL 1847-56, 1858, 1860-7.

Eccles, *1918>*. BL 1937-8, 1947>; *SLH* 1929 (Eccles only?), Eccles & Swinton 1930-9, 1945> (Eccles only?).

Lancaster, *1832-67*. BL 1857-66; *Lancaster Central Lib* 1832, 1834-77, 1882, 1884-88, 1909-15, 1918, 1924, 1927, 1930, 1933-39; 1948 (incl. servicemen); 1949>.

Leigh, *1918>*. BL 1937-8, 1947>; *Leigh Lib* 1918, 1926-31, 1933-4, 1936-7, 1945, 1947, 1949> [?if all Leigh Borough]; *Wigan RO* 1834-9.

Liverpool, *1832-85*. BL 1852-68; *LL* 1832-85 (and 1832-44 MS); *SoG* 1840.

Liverpool, Abercrombie Div., *1885-1918*. BL 1885/6; *LL* 1885-1918.

Liverpool, East Toxteth Div., *1885-1948*. BL 1885/6, 1937-8, 1947-8; *LL* 1885-1915, 1918-39, 1945-8.

Liverpool, Edge Hill Div., *1918>*. BL 1937-8, 1947>; *LL* 1918-39, 1945>.

Liverpool, Everton Div., *1885-1948*. BL 1885/6, 1937-1938, 1947-8; *LL* 1885-1915, 1918-39, 1948.

Liverpool, Exchange Div., *1885>, BL 1885/6, 1937-1938, 1947>; *LL* 1885-1915, 1918-39, 1945>.

Liverpool, Fairfield Div., *1918-48*. BL 1937-8, 1947-1948; *LL* 1885-1915, 1918-39, 1945-8.

Liverpool, Kirkdale Div., *1885>. BL 1885/6, 1937-38, 1947>; *LL* 1885-1915, 1918-39, 1945>.

Liverpool, Scotland, *1885>*. BL 1885/6, 1937-8, 1947>; *LL* 1885-1915, 1918-39, 1945>.

Liverpool, Walton Div., *1885>*. BL 1885/6, 1937-8, 1947>; *LL* 1885-1915, 1918-39, 1945->.

Liverpool, Wavertree Div., *1918>*. BL 1937-8, 1947>; *LL* 1885-1915, 1918-39, 1945>.

Liverpool, West Derby Div., *1885>*. BL 1885/6, 1937-1938, 1947>; *LL* 1885-1915, 1918-39, 1945>.

Liverpool, West Toxteth Div., *1885-1948*. BL 1885/6, 1937-8, 1947-8; *LL* 1885-1915, 1918-39, 1945-8.

Manchester, *1832-85*. BL 1852-3, 1856-7, 1863; *MCL* 1832-85.

Manchester East Div., *1885-1918*. BL 1885/6; *MCL* 1885-1915.

Manchester North Div., *1885-1918*. BL 1885/6; *MCL* 1885-1915.

Manchester North East Div., *1885-1918*. BL 1885/6; *MCL* 1885-1915.

Manchester North West Div., *1885-1918*. BL 1885/6; *MCL* 1885-1915.

Manchester South Div., *1885-1918*. BL 1885/6; *MCL* 1885-1915.

Manchester South West Div., *1885-1918*. BL 1885/6; *MCL* 1885-1915.

Manchester, Ardwick Div., *1918>*. BL 1937-8, 1947>; *MCL* 1918-39, 1945>.

Manchester, Blackley Div., *1918>*. BL 1937-8, 1947>; *MCL* 1918-39, 1945>.

Manchester, Clayton Div., *1918>*. BL 1937-8, 1947>; *MCL* 1918-39, 1945>.

Manchester, Exchange Div., *1918>*. BL 1937-8, 1947>; *MCL* 1918-39, 1945>.

Manchester, Gorton Div., *1918>*. BL 1937-8, 1947>; *MCL* 1918-39, 1945>.

Manchester, Hulme Div., *1918-48*. BL 1937-8, 1947-1948; *MCL* 1918-39, 1945-8.

Manchester, Moss Side Div., *1918>*. BL 1937-8, 1947>; *MCL* 1918-39, 1945>.

Manchester, (Miles) Platting Div., *1918-48*. BL 1937-8, 1947-8; *MCL* 1918-39, 1945-8.

Manchester, Rusholme Div., *1918-48*. BL 1937-8, 1947-8; *MCL* 1918-39, 1945-8.

Manchester, Withington Div., *1918>*. BL 1937-8, 1947>; *MCL* 1918-39, 1945>.

Nelson & Colne, *1918>*. BL 1937, 1947>.

Oldham, *1832-1948*. BL 1854-73, 1875, 1877, 1879-1891, 1893-4, 1896-1900, 1902-15, Aut. 1919-31, 1937-8, 1947-8; *LRO* 1912-3 Chadderton, Crompton, Royton only; *Oldham Local Studies & Archives* 1870-1915, 1918-39, 1945>; *TNA* 1873.

Preston, *1832-1948*. BL 1843-87, 1889-1915, 1918-1923, Aut. 1924-31, 1937-8, 1947-8; *GL* 1868; *Preston Central Lib* 1832-42, 1845-6, 1861, 1863-1866, 1868, 1870, 1879, 1880, 1882-1915, 1918-22, 1929-39, 1945>; *LRO* 1912-15, 1939-40 (part).

Rochdale, *1832>*. BL 1857-63, 1885/6-90, 1937-8, 1947>; *Rochdale Central Lib* 1832 (with poll added), 1834, 1836-7, 1840, 1843-45, 1847-71, 1874, 1914, 1933-9, 1945>. Castleton only 1850 (see J. Cole., *Tracing your Ancestors through Local Libraries* (1983) [Rochdale, Middleton, Heywood]).

Lancashire: *Boroughs* continued

Rossendale, *1918>*. *BL* 1937-8, 1947>; *LRO* 1918-1940, 1945>; *Bacup Lib* 1937-9 Bacup only; *Rawtenstall Lib* 'To 1931' [sic] Rawtenstall, Piercy polling district only.

St Helens, *1885>*. *BL* 1885/6, 1937-8, 1947>; *St Helens Community Leisure Dept* 1885-1915, 1918-39, 1945> (with burgess rolls).

Salford, *1832-1918*. *BL* 1862-5, 1868/9-74, 1876-80, 1885/6-92, 1894, 1897-1915; *MCL* 1853, 1855, 1864, 1866-9, 1872, 1875, 1877-1883, 1885, 1889, 1898, 1900-7, 1913; *SLH* 1842, 1857, 1861-72, 1874, 1876-9, 1883-85, 1900; 1900-14 (gaps, uncatalogued); 1918-39, 1945>.

Salford North Div., *1918-48*. *BL* 1918-31, 1937-8, 1947-8; *SLH* 1918-39, 1945>.

Salford South Div., *1918-48*. *BL* 1918-31, 1937-8, 1947-8; *SLH* 1918-39, 1945>.

Salford West Div., *1918>*. *BL* 1918-31, 1937-8, 1947>; *SLH* 1918-39, 1945>.

Southport, *1918>*. *BL* 1937-8, 1947>.

Stalybridge, *1868-1918*. *BL* None; *TLS* 1915 Waterloo only.

Stockport, *1832-1948*. *See under Cheshire.*

Warrington (Cheshire until 1918), ***1832>***. *BL* 1859-1866, 1868/9-72, 1875-6, 1879-80, 1885/6, 1937-8, 1947>; *LRO* 1832; *WCL* 1832-1914, 1918-21, 1924-1939, 1945> (incl. revisions 1874-94, 1899).

Wigan, *1832>*. *BL* 1885/6, 1918-31, 1937-8, 1947>; *Wigan RO* 1836-41 (MS); 1861-55, 1920-7, 1929.

Burgess Rolls

Aston-under-Lyne. *BL* 1896/97.

Bamford and Norden. *Rochdale Central Lib* 1934, 1936, 1938.

Barrow in Furness. *Cumbria R.O., Barrow* 1867-8; *Barrow Lib* 1868-9.

Bolton. *Bolton Ref Lib* 1838-1914 (1872 with part Rumworth; 1877 with part Halliwell; 1898 with area).

Burnley. *Burnley Lib* 1861 (MS); 1890-1904, 1908, 1910-14;

Bury. *Bury Lib* 1876-1902, 1904-15 (then merged); jury list: 1830.

Haslingden. *Haslingden Lib.* 1893, 1899, 1905, 1910; Haslingden and Helmshore. Owners and occupiers: 1891, 1895-6, 1900, 1905, 1909-10, 1914.

Heywood. *Heywood Lib* 1887, 1900-1, 1904-6.

Liverpool. *LL* 1835-58 (MS); 1835-72; *GL* 1837.

Manchester. *MCL* 1838-1914.

Oldham. *Oldham Local Studies & Archives* 1849-1873, 1881 (of which only 1851-71 published).

Preston. *Preston Central Lib* 1397-1682 (publ. Record Society of Lancashire and Cheshire **9** (1884)); 1844, 1847, 1851, 1863.

Rawtenstall (part of Rossendale) *LRO* 1891-1915.

St Helens. *St Helens Community Leisure Dept* 1874-1915, 1918-39.

Salford. *MCL* 1852-66, 1868-76, 1878-88, 1890-4, 1896, 1898, 1901-4, 1907-12, 1914; *SLH* 1859-68, 1871, 1876-8, 1881, 1884.

Warrington. *WCL* 1847-80 (except 1866).

Wigan. *Wigan RO* (and admission certificates) 1694-1832, 1835-40, 1865.

Freemen

Lancaster. *Lancaster Central Lib* 1688-1840 (publ. Record Society of Lancashire and Cheshire **87**, **90** (1935, 1938)); *LRO* 1688-1895.

Parochial Registers

Burnley. *Burnley Lib* parochial registers: 1895-1902, 1904, 1911-13.

Salford. *SLH* 1889.

County voters' and jury lists

Warrington. *WCL* 1885-94, 1897-9, 1901-14.

Post-1948 ER holdings at *BL, LL, LRO, MCL, SLH, TLS, WCL,* and *Accrington, Bacup, Barrow, Blackburn, Bolton, Burnley, Bury, Haslingden, Heywood, Huyton, Lancaster, Leigh, Middleton, Morecambe, Oldham, Preston, Prestwich, Radcliffe, Rawtenstall, Rochdale, St Helens (Community Leisure Dept)* and *Whalley (Central) Libraries, Cheshire & Chester Archives & Local Studies, Chester, Cumbria Record Office: Barrow* and *Kendal,* and *Wigan Record Office.*

LEICESTERSHIRE

Abbreviations

BL = British Library.
GL = Guildhall Library, London.
LRO = The Record Office for Leicestershire, Leicester and Rutland, Wigston Magna.

County Constituencies

1832-85

Leicestershire, Northern Div. *BL* 1832, 1844-84; *LRO* 1832, 1834-5, 1841-59; *GL* 1832, 1841; 1874.

Leicestershire, Southern Div. *BL* 1832, 1864-84; *LRO* 1834-5, 1841-59; 1874.

1885-1918

Eastern or **Melton Div.** *BL* 1885/6-1915; *LRO* 1885-6, 1891-3, 1895-1915;

Mid or **Loughborough Div.** *BL* 1885/6-1915; *LRO* 1885-6, 1891-3, 1895-1915;

Southern or **Harborough Div.** *BL* 1885/6-1915; *LRO* 1885-6, 1891-3, 1895-1915;

Western or **Bosworth Div.** *BL* 1885/6-1915; *LRO* 1885-6, 1891-3, 1895-1915;

1918-48

Bosworth Div. *BL* 1921-31, 1937-8, 1947-8; *LRO* 1918-39, 1945-8.

Harborough Div. *BL* 1921-31, 1937-8, 1947-8; *LRO* 1918-39, 1945-8.

Loughborough Div. *BL* 1921-31, 1937-8, 1947-8; *LRO* 1918-39, 1945-8.

Melton Div. *BL* 1921-31, 1937-8, 1947-8; *LRO* 1918-39, 1945-8.

Leicestershire continued

Borough Constituencies
Leicester, *1832-1918*. BL 1835-46, 1848-50, 1852-66,
1868-70, 1885/6-1902, 1905-15;
LRO 1833-5, 1844-63, 1865, 1868, 1874-1900.
Leicester, East Div., *1918-48*. BL 1918-31, 1937-8,
1947-8; *LRO* 1921, 1926-39, 1945-8.
Leicester, South Div., *1918-48*. BL 1918-31, 1937-8,
1947-8; *LRO* 1921, 1926-39, 1945-8.
Leicester, West Div., *1918-48*. BL 1918-31, 1937-8,
1947-8; *LRO* 1921, 1926-39, 1945-8.

Burgess Rolls
Leicester. *LRO* 1894, 1907, 1909, 1914.

Freemen
Leicester. *LRO* 1196-1930 (pubd., *Register of the
Freemen of Leicester 1196-1930*, ed. H. Hartopp,
2 vols., [1927/1933]; Register of the Freemen of
Leicester 1931-1985 [1987])).

Post-1948 ER holdings at *BL*, *LRO* and
Swadlincote Library (Derbys.).

LINCOLNSHIRE

Abbreviations
BL = British Library.
GL = Guildhall Library, London.
GmL = Grantham Library.
LA = Lincolnshire Archives, Lincoln.
LCL = Lincoln Central Library.
NEL = North East Lincolnshire Archives, Grimsby.
SoG = Society of Genealogists.
STH = Stamford Town Hall.

County Constituencies

1832-67
Lincolnshire, Parts of Holland and Kesteven, or
Southern Div. *BL* 1842-66 (1848, 1864-6 Pts
Holland only, 1857 Pts Kesteven only);
LA Kesteven: returns 1832-42, 1845-50, 1853-66;
registers 1834-45, 1847-53, 1857-8, 1860-2, 1864-6;
LCL 1832 (Kesteven only);
GL 1832, 1834, 1838, 1840.
Lincolnshire, Parts of Lindsey, or **Northern Div.**
BL 1832, 1834-7, 1840-2, 1847, 1849-50, 1852,
1855-7, 1859-65, 1867; *LA* 1832-67.

1867-85
Mid Lincolnshire Div. (Pts Kesteven, Lindsey).
BL 1868-1878 (Pts Lindsey only);
LA 1867-72 (Lindsey only), 1874-84; 1874.
North Lincolnshire Div. (Pts Lindsey). **BL** 1868-1878;
LA 1867-84; 1874.
South Lincolnshire Div. (Pts Holland, Kesteven).
BL None; *GmL* 1868, 1874 (Harrowby, Manthorpe-
cum-Little Gonerby, Spittlegate, Houghton and
Walton); 1874.

1885-1918
Holland or **Spalding Div. *BL*** 1889; *LA* 1904;
North Kesteven or **Sleaford Div. *BL*** None;
LA 1904; 1913-6 [sic].

Lincolnshire continued

South Kesteven or **Stamford Div. *BL*** None;
LA 1904; Grantham Borough only 1915;
GmL Grantham [Borough ?] only 1888-9, 1891,
1894-1914 (incl. burgesses).
East Lindsey or **Louth Div. *BL*** None;
LA 1889, 1893-5, 1899-1907; 1908 (draft); 1911
(part); 1913-5;
North Lindsey or **Brigg Div. *BL*** None; *LA* 1894-5,
1899-1901, 1903-8 (also 1908 draft), 1911, 1913-5.
South Lindsey or **Horncastle Div. *BL*** None[?];
LA 1889, 1893-5, 1899-1907; 1908 (draft); 1911,
1913-5,
West Lindsey or **Gainsborough Div. *BL*** None;
LA 1890 [FL2 Box]; 1893-5, 1900-7, 1911, 1913-5,

1918-48
Brigg Div. (Pts Lindsey). **BL** 1937-8, 1947-8; *LA*
1919-1931, 1933-4, 1939, 1945-8 [1918-9, 1935-7].
Gainsborough Div. (Pts Lindsey). **BL** 1937-8, 1947-8;
LA 1919-1931, 1933-39 [?], 1945-8.
Grantham Div. (Pts Lindsey). **BL** Aut. 1921-31, 1937-
1938, 1947-8; *LA* 1918-30, 1932-9, 1945-8 (also
AVL 1920-7, 1930, 1932-4, 1936-9 and Wartime);
GmL 1920-3, 1929-32, 1934-9 [all Grantham only?]
Holland with Boston Div. (Pts Holland) *BL* 1937-8,
1947-8;
Horncastle Div. (Pts Lindsey). **BL** 1937-8, 1947-8;
LA 1919-1931, 1933-4, 1939, 1945-8 [1918-9, 1935-
1938].
Louth Div. (Pts Lindsey). **BL** 1937-8, 1947-8; *LA*
1919-1931, 1933-4, 1939, 1945-8 [1918-9, 1836-8].
Rutland & Stamford Div. (Pts Kesteven, Rutland
Administrative County). **BL** Aut. 1921-31, 1937-8,
1947-8; *LA* 1919-39, 1945-8 (also AVL 1918-26, 1929,
1931-2, 1934-9); *STH* possible holdings.

Borough Constituencies
Boston, *1832-1918*. BL 1857-63, 1885, 1897;
Boston Town Hall 1830[sic]-1914; *SoG* 1867.
Grantham, *1832-85*. BL 1885/6, 1897 [sic?];
GmL 1868, 1874; 1874.
Great Grimsby, *1832-1918*. BL 1885/6-1915;
NEL 1863 (MS); 1868, 1873-1915; *Grimsby Lib*
1901-15.
Grimsby, *1918>*. BL 1918-31, 1937-8, 1947>;
NEL 1918-39, 1945>; *Grimsby Lib* 1918-39, 1945>.
Lincoln, *1832>*. BL 1862-1910, 1937-8, 1947>;
LA 1913, 1914 (Castle and Bracebridge Wards
only), 1918-22, 1924-26, 1930, 1932-39, 1945>.
Municipal elections (various wards) 1898-1905; *LCL*
1909-14, 1920, 1922-39, 1945>.
Stamford, *1832-85*. BL 1843-72;
STH 1832-7, 'to 1899'; *Burghley House
Preservation Trust, Stamford* 1832-60.

Burgess Rolls
Grimsby. *NEL* 1873-1915.
Lincoln. *LA* 1860-2.
Stamford. *STH* 1835 'to 1863', 1835-8 'to 1914-5'
(St Mary's and All Saints' Wards only).

Lincolnshire continued

Freemen
Grimsby. *NEL* 1780-1980 (published 1994, from *NEL*).
Lincoln. *LA* 1907-8 (some missing?), 1912.

Post-1948 ER holdings at *BL, LA, LCL, NEL,* and *Gainsborough* and *Grimsby Libraries.*

LONDON, MIDDLESEX & WESTMINSTER
See also under Essex, Kent and Surrey.

Abbreviations

BL	=	British Library.
BsL	=	Battersea Library, 265 Lavender Hill, SW11. Bexley, Bromley – *see under* Kent.
ChL	=	Chelsea Library, Kings Road, SW3.
CLH	=	Camden Local History Library, Holborn, WC1.
CWA	=	City of Westminster Archives Centre, 10 St Ann's Street, Westminster, SW1P.
ECL	=	Ealing Central Library, Ealing Broadway, W5.
ELH	=	Enfield Local History Unit, Southgate Town Hall, Green Lanes, N13.
FL	=	Finsbury Library, 245 St John Street, EC1.
GL	=	Guildhall Library, Aldermanbury, EC2P 2EJ.
GrLH	=	Greenwich Local History Library, SE3.
HA	=	Hackney Archives Department, Rose Lipman Library, De Beauvoir Street, N1.
HFA	=	Hammersmith & Fulham Archives, The Lilla Huset, 191 Talgarth Road, W6.
HL	=	Holborn Library, 32-38 Theobalds Road, WC2X 8PA.
ICL	=	Islington Central Library, 2 Fieldway Crescent, N5.
KL	=	Kensington Library, Phillimore Walk, W8.
LA	=	Lambeth Archives, Minet Library, Knatchbull Road, SE5.
LMA	=	London Metropolitan Archives, 40 Northampton Road, EC1R 0HB. Merton, Morden Libraries – see under Surrey. Newham LS Library – see under Essex.
SLS	=	Southwark Local Studies Library, 211 Borough High Street, SE1.
SoG	=	Society of Genealogists.
THL	=	Tower Hamlets Local History Library, 277 Bancroft Road, E1. Waltham Forest LS – see under Essex.
TNA	=	The National Archives, Kew.

LONDON
Borough Constituencies
City of London, *1832-1948*. *BL* 1832, 1840, 1848, 1859-70, 1873-1915, 1918-31, 1937-8, 1947-8; *Corporation of London Record Office* 1840, 1872-1896, 1898-1902, 1904-15, 1918-39, 1945-8; Common Hall registers: 1887-date (1940/1 missing). Ward registers: 1946 (Aldgate only); 1947 (except Cheap & Lime St.); 1948 (except Aldgate & Tower); *GL* 1832-1915, 1918-39, 1945-8. Index to 1853; Common Hall electorate: 1887>; Freemen inhabitant householders: 1846; St. Mary Aldermanbury: 1847-1851, 1874; St. Mary Woolnoth: 1832; Individual Wards: Aldgate 1849-52; Billingsgate 1850 (MS); Bishopsgate 1859; Bridge Within 1865-66; Farringdon Within 1849; Farringdon Without 1849, 1854-55; Lime Street 1849 (MS), 1850-65, 1867-92; *LMA* 1834-5(?), 1837, 1855; *SoG* 1836 (incomplete).

All other constituencies were boroughs in London Administrative County, created in 1889. For convenience these are shown from the constituency boundary changes of 1885. For the period before 1885 see also Middlesex, Surrey and Kent.

Battersea & Clapham, Battersea Div., *1885-1918*. *BL* 1897; *LMA* 1890[?]-1915; *BsL* 1885-1915.

Battersea & Clapham, Clapham Div., *1885-1918*. *BL* 1897; *LMA* 1890[?]-1915; *BsL* 1885-1915.

Battersea, North Div., *1918>*. *BL* 1937-8, 1947>; *LMA* 1918-39, 1945>; *BsL* 1919-39, 1945>.

Battersea, South Div., *1918>*. *BL* 1937-8, 1947>; *LMA* 1918-39, 1945>; *BsL* 1919-39, 1945.

Bermondsey: Rotherhithe, *1918-48*. *BL* 1937-9, 1945-8; *LMA* 1918-39, 1945-8; *SLS* 1918-39, 1945-1948.

Bermondsey: West Bermondsey, *1918-48*. *BL* 1937-9, 1945-1948; *LMA* 1918-39, 1945-8; *SLS* 1918-39, 1945-8.

Bethnal Green: North East, *1885-1948*. *BL* 1897-8, 1900, 1937-8, 1947-8; *LMA* 1885-1915, 1918-39, 1945-8; *THL* 1901-15, 1918-39, 1945-8.

Bethnal Green: South West, *1885-1948*. *BL* 1897-8, 1900, 1937-8, 1947-8; *LMA* 1885-1915, 1918-39, 1945-8; *THL* 1901-15, 1918-39, 1945-8.

Bexley – *see under* Kent.

Bromley – *see under* Kent.

Camberwell, Dulwich, *1885>*. *BL* 1897-1901, 1937-1939, 1945 (May, Oct), 1946 (Oct), 1947>; *LMA* 1890-1915, 1918-39, 1945>; *SLS* 1897.

Camberwell, North, *1885-1948*. *BL* 1897-1901, 1937-39, 1945 (May, Oct), 1946 (Oct), 1947-8; *LMA* 1890-1915, 1918-39, 1945-1948; *SLS* 1898.

Camberwell, North-West, *1918-48*. *BL* [1897-1901?] 1937-9, 1945 (May, Oct), 1946 (Oct), 1947-8; *LMA* 1918-39, 1945-8; *SLS* 1913-5, 1918-39, 1945>.

Camberwell, Peckham, *1885>*. *BL* 1897-1901, 1937-1939, 1945 (May, Oct), 1946 (Oct), 1947>; *LMA* 1890-1915, 1918-39, 1945>; *SLS* 1901 (MF).

London continued

Chelsea, *1885>* (pre-1885, *see* Middlesex). *BL* 1897-
1900, 1937-8, 1947>; *LMA* 1885[?]-1915, 1918-39,
1945>; *ChL* 1885, 1887, 1889, 1891-1915, 1918-39
(1918-9 incl. AVL), 1945-8; Hans Town *c.*1880's.

Deptford, 1885> (Kent until 1889). *BL* 1885/6, 1888-
1891, 1897, 1937-8, 1947>; *LMA* 1890-1915, 1918-
1939, 1945>.

Finsbury, pre-1885 – *see under* Middlesex.

Finsbury, Central Div., *1885-1918*. *BL* 1891-1915;
LMA 1890-1915; *FL* 1901-15; Clerkenwell 1885.

Finsbury, East Div., *1885-1918*. *BL* 1891-1915;
LMA 1885-1915; *FL* 1901-15; Finsbury St. Luke
only 1885.

Finsbury, Holborn Div., *1885-1918*. *BL* 1891-1915;
LMA 1885-1915; *FL* 1901-15; Holborn (?all div.)
1885; *HL* 1878, 1893-1900 (all MF); 1901-15.

Finsbury, *1918-48*. *BL* 1918-31, 1937-8, 1947-8;
LMA 1918-39, 1945-8; *FL* 1918-39, 1945-8.

Fulham, *1885-1918*. *BL* 1897-1901; *LMA* 1885-
1915; *HFA* 1885, 1887-91, 1895-1915; jury lists
1902-3, 1905, 1909-12, 1921.

Fulham, East, *1918>*. *BL* 1937-8, 1947>; *LMA* 1918-
1939, 1945>; *HFA* 1919-39 (incl. AVL 1918-9),
1945>.

Fulham, West, *1918>*. *BL* 1937-8, 1947>;
LMA 1918-1939, 1945>; *HFA* 1927-39, 1945>.

Greenwich, *1889>* (*see under* Kent before 1889).
BL 1900, 1937-8, 1947>;
LMA 1890-1915, 1918-39, 1945>;
GrLH 1892-4, 1898; 1899 (occupiers); 1900; 1901-
1905 (occupiers); 1906, 1908, 1910-2, 1915; 1918-9
(AVL); 1931-2, 1934; 1935 (A-M only); 1936-8,
1945>.

Hackney, *see under* Middlesex pre-1885.

Hackney, Central Div., *1885-1948*. *BL* 1897-1901,
1937-38, 1947-8; *LMA* 1890-1915, 1918-39, 1945-
1948.

Hackney, North Div., *1885-1948*. *BL* 1897-1901,
1937-38, 1947-8; *LMA* 1890-1915, 1918-39, 1945-
1948; *FL* Stoke Newington 1885.

Hackney, South Div., *1885-1948*. *BL* 1897-1901,
1937-38, 1947-8; *LMA* 1890-1915, 1918-39, 1945-
1948.

Hammersmith, *1885-1918*. *BL* 1897-1915;
LMA 1885-1915; *HFA* 1886, 1889, 1890-1915.

Hammersmith, North Div., *1918>*. *BL* 1918-31,
1937-1938, 1947>; *LMA* 1918-39, 1945>;
HFA 1920-34, 1936-9, 1945>.

Hammersmith, South Div., *1918>*. *BL* 1918-31,
1937-1938, 1947>; *LMA* 1918-39, 1945>;
HFA 1918-39 (+ 1939 'Supplementary').

Hampstead, *1885>*. *BL* 18978, 1937-8, 1947>;
LMA 1885-1915, 1918-39, 1945>;
CLH 1899-1915, 1918-39, 1945>;

Holborn, *1918-48*. *BL* 1937-8, 1947-8; *LMA* 1918-
1939, 1945-1948; *HL* 1918-39, 1945-8.

Islington, East Div., *1885>*. *BL* 1897-01, 1937-8,
1947>; *LMA* 1885-1915, 1918-39, 1945>;
ICL 1885-1915, 1918-39, 1945>.

Islington, North Div., *1885>*. *BL* 1897-01, 1937-8,
1947>; *LMA* 1890-1915, 1918-39, 1945>.

Islington, South Div., *1885-1948*. *BL* 1897-01,
1937-1938; *LMA* 1890-1915, 1918-39, 1945-8;
ICL 1885-1915, 1918-39, 1945>.

Islington, West Div., *1885-1948*. *BL* 1897-01, 1937-
1938, 1947-8; *LMA* 1885-1915, 1918-39, 1945-8;
ICL 1885-1915, 1918-39, 1945>.

Kensington, North Div., *1885>*. *BL* 1897-1902,
1937-7, 1947>; *LMA* 1885-1915, 1918-39, 1945>;
KL 1890-1905, 1908-15; 1918 (incl. AVL); 1919-39,
1945>.

Kensington, South Div., *1885>*. *BL* 1897-1902,
1937-7, 1947>; *LMA* 1885-1915, 1918-39, 1945>;
KL 1890-1905, 1908-15; 1918 (incl. AVL); 1919-39,
1945>.

Lambeth, *see under* Surrey pre-1885.

Lambeth: Brixton Div., *1885>*. *BL* 1897-1901, 1937-
1938, 1945>; *LMA* 1890-1915, 1918-39, 1945>.

Lambeth: Kennington Div., *1885-1948*. *BL* 1897-
1901, 1937-8, 1945-8; *LMA* 1890-1915, 1918-39,
1945-8.

Lambeth: North Div., *1885-1948*. *BL* 1897-1901,
1937-8, 1945-8; *LMA* 1890-1915, 1918-39, 1945-8.

Lambeth: Norwood Div., *1885>*. *BL* 1897-1901,
1937-8, 1945>; *LMA* 1890-1915, 1918-39, 1945>.

Lewisham, *1885-1918*. *BL* 1885/6-89, 1897, 1899;
LMA 1890-1915.

Lewisham, East Div., *1918-48*. *BL* 1937-8, 1947-8;
LMA 1918-39, 1945-8.

Lewisham, West Div., *1918>*. *BL* 1937-8, 1947>;
LMA 1918-39, 1945>.

Marylebone – *see* St. Marylebone.

Newington, Walworth Div., *1885-1918*. *BL* 1906-14;
SLS 1885-1900.

Newington, West Div., *1885-1918*. *BL* 1906-14;
SLS 1885-1900.

Paddington, North Div., *1885>*. *BL* 1897-1901
1904-1906, 1908-10, 1914-5, 1919-31, 1937-8,
1947>; *LMA* 1885-1915, 1918-39, 1945>;
CWA 1902-15, 1918-39, 1945>.

Paddington, South Div., *1885>*. *BL* 897-1901 1904-
1906, 1908-10, 1914-5, 1919-31, 1937-8, 1947>;
LMA 1885-1915, 1918-39, 1945>; *CWA* 1902-15,
1918-39, 1945>.

Poplar, Bow & Bromley Div., *1918-48*. *BL* 1937-8,
1947-8; *LMA* 1918-39, 1945-8; *THL* 1918-39,
1945-1948.

Poplar, South Poplar Div., *1918-48*. *BL* 1937-8,
1947-8; *LMA* 1918-39, 1945-8.

St. George Hanover Square, *1885-1918*. *BL* 1885/6,
1892-1900, 1902-4; *LMA* 1885-1915.

St. Marylebone, East Div., *1885-1918*. *BL* None;
LMA 1885-1915; *CWA* 1905.

St. Marylebone, West Div., *1885-1918*. *BL* None;
LMA 1885-1915; *CWA* 1905, 1912.

St. Marylebone, *1918>*. *BL* 1937-8, 1947>;
LMA 1918-39, 1945>; *CWA* 1918-39, 1945>.

St. Pancras, East Div., *1885-1918*. *BL* 1905-15;
LMA 1885-1915; *CLH* 1886-97 (MF), 1899-1915.

London continued

St. Pancras, North Div., *1885>*. *BL* 1905-15, 1918-1931, 1937-8, 1947>; *LMA* 1885-1915, 1918-39, 1945>; *CLH* 1886-1897 (MF), 1899-1915, 1918-39, 1945>.

St. Pancras, South Div., *1885-1918*. *BL* 1905-15; *LMA* 1885-1915; *CLH* 1886-97 (MF), 1899-1915.

St. Pancras, West Div., *1885-1918*. *BL* 1905-15; *LMA* 1890-1915; *CLH* 1886-97 (MF), 1899-1915.

St. Pancras, South East Div., *1918-48*. *BL* 1918-1931, 1937-8, 1947-8; *LMA* 1918-39, 1945-8; *CLH* 1918-39, 1945-8.

St. Pancras, South West Div., *1918-48*. *BL* 1918-1931, 1937-8, 1947-8; *LMA* 1918-39, 1945-8; *CLH* 1918-39, 1945-8.

Shoreditch, Haggerston Div., *1885-1918*. *BL* None; *LMA* 1885-1915.

Shoreditch, Hoxton Div., *1885-1918*. *BL* None; *LMA* 1885-1915.

Shoreditch, *1918-48*. *BL* 1937-8, 1947-8; *LMA* 1918-1939, 1945>.

Southwark – *before 1885 see under* Surrey.

Southwark, Bermondsey Div., *1885-1918*. *BL* 1885/6-90; *LMA* 1890-1915; *SLS* 1887-1915.

Southwark, Rotherhithe Div., *1885-1918*. *BL* 1885/6-90; *LMA* 1890-1915; *SLS* 1885-1915.

Southwark, West Div., *1885-1918*. *BL* 1885/6-90; *LMA* 1890-1915; *SLS* 1894-1915.

Southwark, Central Div., *1918-48*. *BL* 1937-8, 1947-1948; *LMA* 1918-39, 1945-8; *SLS* 1918-39, 1945-8.

Southwark, North Div., *1918-48*. *BL* 1937-9, 1947-1948; *LMA* 1918-39, 1945-8; *SLS* 1918-39, 1945-8.

Southwark, South East Div., *1918-48*. *BL* 1937-9, 1947-8; *LMA* 1918-39, 1945-8; *SLS* 1918-39, 1945-1948.

Stepney – *before 1918, see* Tower Hamlets.

Stepney, Limehouse Div. (incl. Ratcliff), *1918-48*. *BL* 1918-23, Aut. 1924-31, 1937-8, 1947-8; *LMA* 1918-39, 1945-1948; *THL* 1918-39, 1945-8.

Stepney, Mile End Div., *1918-48*. *BL* 1918-23, Aut. 1924-31, 1937-8, 1947-8; *LMA* 1918-39, 1945-1948; *THL* 1918-39, 1945-8.

Stepney, Whitechapel & St. George's Div., *1918-1948*. *BL* 1918-23, Aut. 1924-31, 1937-8, 1947-8; *LMA* 1918-39, 1945-8; *THL* 1918-39, 1945-8.

Stoke Newington, *1918-48*. *BL* 1930-1, 1937-8, 1947-8; *LMA* 1918-39, 1945-8.

Strand, *1885-1918*. *BL* 1885/6, 1892-1900, 1902-4; *LMA* 1885-1915.

Tower Hamlets, Bow & Bromley Div., *1885-1918*. *BL* 1897-1915; *LMA* 1885-1915; *THL* 1898, 1901-1915; Bow only 1894-5.

Tower Hamlets, Limehouse Div., *1885-1918*. *BL* 1897-1915; *LMA* 1885-1915; *THL* 1901-15.

Tower Hamlets, Mile End Div., *1885-1918*. *BL* 1897-1915; *LMA* 1885-1915; *THL* 1901-15.

Tower Hamlets, Poplar Div., *1885-1918*. *BL* 1897-1915; *LMA* 1885-1915; *THL* 1901-15.

Tower Hamlets, St George Div., *1885-1918*. *BL* 1897-1915; *LMA* 1885-1915; *THL* 1901-15.

Tower Hamlets, Stepney Div., *1885-1918*. *BL* 1897-1915; *LMA* 1885-1915.

Tower Hamlets, Whitechapel Div., *1885-1918*. *BL* 1897-1915; *LMA* 1885-1915.

University of London, *1867-48*. *BL* None; *LMA* 1945.

Wandsworth, *1885-1918*. *BL* None; *LMA* 1890-1915; *BsL* 1898-1900, 1907-14.

Wandsworth, Balham & Tooting Div., *1918-48*. *BL* 1937-8, 1947-8; *LMA* 1918-39, 1945-8; *BsL* 1918-39, 1945-9.

Wandsworth, Central Div., *1918>*. *BL* 1937-8, 1947>; *LMA* 1918-39, 1945>; *BsL* 1918-39, 1945-9.

Wandsworth, Clapham Div., *1918>*. *BL* 1937-8, 1947>; *LMA* 1918-39, 1945>; *BsL* 1918-39, 1945-9.

Wandsworth, Putney Div., *1918>*. *BL* 1937-8, 1947>; *LMA* 1918-39, 1945>; *BsL* 1918-39, 1945-9.

Wandsworth, Streatham Div., *1918>*. *BL* 1937-8, 1947>; *LMA* 1918-39, 1945>; *BsL* 1918-39, 1945-9.

Westminster – *see under* Middlesex pre-1885.

Westminster, *1885-1918*. *BL* 1892-1900, 1902-4; *LMA* 1885-1915; *CWA* 1906-14; St Margaret & St John only 1888.

Westminster, Abbey Div., *1918-48*. *BL* 1937-8, 1947-8; *LMA* 1918-39, 1945-8; *CWA* 1939.

Westminster, St George's Div., *1918-48*. *BL* 1937-8, 1947-8; *LMA* 1918-39, 1945-8; *CWA* 1939-41 (MS).

Woolwich, *1885-1918*. *BL* None; *LMA* 1890-1915; *GrLH* 1900-14.

Woolwich, East Div., *1918>*. *BL* 1937-8, 1947>. *GrLH* 1919, 1921, 1923, 1925, 1934-9, 1945>.

Woolwich, West Div., *1918>*. *BL* 1937-8, 1947>;. *GrLH* 1919, 1921, 1923, 1925, 1934-9, 1945>.

MIDDLESEX

County Constituencies

1832-85

Middlesex. *BL* Tottenham only 1861, 1862, 1865-74, 1878-9; *GL* 1837, 1860-3, 1868, 1870-84; St John Hampstead only 1860; Tottenham only 1861-2; *LMA* 1832-42, 1883-5; overseas returns of electors 1847-82; 1874.
CLH St Pancras (county voters only) 1866;
ChL St Luke's, Chelsea 1863;
ELH Edmonton only 1833; Enfield only 1832, 1837 (copy); Edmonton & Enfield 1862, 1865-6, 1868, 1870, 1872-4, 1878-9 (copies);
HFA 1837-8, 1844-6, 1880;
HL St. Andrew Holborn (Within). Middlesex County electorate: 1843, 1855, 1851 (all MF).
THL 1834 (Tower Hamlets indexed); Ratcliff, 1838-9, 1841-54; *SoG* 1840; *TNA*. 1874.

1885-1918

Brentford Div. *BL* 1889-1915; *LMA* 1885-1915;
ECL Norwood North only 1913;
SoG Hanwell only 1902 (parochial register).
Ealing Div. *BL* 1891-1915; *LMA* 1885-1915;
ECL 1890-7, 1899-1914.
SoG Hanwell only 1902 (parochial register).

Middlesex: *County 1885-1918* continued

Enfield Div. *BL* 1891-1915; *LMA* 1885-1915; *ELH* 1890-7, 1899-1914.
Harrow Div. *BL* 1891-1915; *LMA* 1885-1915.
Hornsey Div. *BL* 1891-1915; *LMA* 1885-1915; *FL* 1885 [all Hornsey div?].
Tottenham Div. *BL* 1891-1915; *LMA* 1885-1915.
Uxbridge Div. *BL* 1891-1915; *LMA* 1885-1915.

1918-48

Acton Div. *BL* Aut. 1921-31, 1937-8, 1947-8; *LMA* ?; *ECL* 1918, 1921-39, 1945-8.
Brentford & Chiswick Div. *BL* Aut. 1921-31, 1937-8, 1947-8; *LMA* 1918-39; *ELH* 1924-39, 1945-8 (1947 incl. Potters Bar).
Enfield Div. *BL* Aut. 1921-31, 1937-8, 1947-8; *LMA* 1918-39.
Finchley Div. *BL* Aut. 1921-31, 1937-8, 1947-8; *LMA* 1918-39.
Harrow Div. *BL* Aut. 1921-31, 1937-8; *LMA* 1918-39.
Hendon Div. *BL* Aut. 1921-31, 1937-8; *LMA* 1918-39.
Spelthorne Div. *BL* Aut. 1921-31, 1937-8, 1947-8; *LMA* 1918-39.
Twickenham Div. *BL* Aut. 1921-31, 1937-8; *LMA* 1918-39.
Uxbridge Div. *BL* Aut. 1921-31, 1937-8, 1947-8; *LMA* 1918-39.
Wood Green Div. *BL* Aut. 1921-31, 1937-8, 1947-8; *LMA* 1918-39.

Borough Constituencies

Chelsea, *1868-89* (thereafter see London). *BL* None; *LMA* 1873(?)-89; *ChL* 1885, 1887, 1889; *HFA* 1881-1885.
Ealing, *1918-45. BL* 1937-8; *LMA* 1922-39.
Ealing, East Div., *1945-8. BL* 1947-8.
Ealing, West Div., *1945-8. BL* 1947-8.
Edmonton, *1918>. BL* 1937-8, 1947>; *LMA* 1922-39; *ELH* 1937-9, 1945>.
Finsbury, *1832-85* (thereafter see London). *BL* 1857-8; *GL* Farringdon Without, Inner and Middle Temple. 1849; St. Andrew Holborn: property owners: 1843, 1850-1, 1854-55; claimants and objections: 1843, 1849(?), 1850-51; St. Bartholomew by the Exchange and St. John Zachary: 1832-37 (both MS); St. George Bloomsbury and St. Giles in the Fields. 1837, 1878; *LMA* 1832, 1865, 1873-85.
FL Parishes etc. of Furnivall's Inn, Staple Inn, Liberty of the Rolls, Gray's Inn, Lincoln's Inn, St. Giles in the Fields, St. Andrew and St. George the Martyr, Holborn, St. George, Bloomsbury, Saffron Hill, Hatton Garden, Liberty of Ely Rents, St. Sepulchre, St. Luke, St. Botolph, Liberty of Glasshouse Yard, St Mary's, Islington, St Mary's, Stoke Newington, and part Hornsey. 1873-85; St. James Clerkenwell. 1842, 1873-85.
HA Stoke Newington 1861, 1879; 1883 (incl. South Hornsey, Islington, Finsbury and Holborn);
HL Holborn. 1837 (St. George Bloomsbury and St. Giles in the Fields only); 1878, 1893-1900 (all MF); 1901-15, 1918-39, 1945-54, 1956, 1960-64;
ICL St Mary Islington 1860.

Hackney, *1868-89* (pre-1868 see Tower Hamlets; after 1889 see under London). *BL* None; *LMA* 1873(?)-89; *HA* 1871, 1879 (incl. Shoreditch & Bethnal Green).
Hammersmith – *see under* London.
Harrow, Central or **West Div.,** *1945>. BL* 1947>.
Harrow, East Div., *1945>. BL* 1947>.
Hendon, North Div., *1945>. BL* 1947>.
Hendon, South Div., *1945>. BL* 1947>.
Heston & Isleworth, *1945>. BL* 1947>.
Hornsey, *1918>. BL* 1937-8, 1947>; *LMA* 1922-39.
Lambeth (Surrey) *1832-85* (thereafter see London). *BL* None; *LA* 1832-85; *SLS* Newington 1833-85.
(St.) Marylebone, *1832-85* (thereafter see London). *BL* None; *LMA* 1873(?)-85; *CLH* 1866-71, 1873-7, 1879-85 (all MF); *CWA* Paddington 1844-7, 1855, 1867, St Marylebone 1844-8, 1850-1, 1854-5.
Southall, *1945>. BL* 1947>.
Southwark (Surrey), *1832-85. BL* None. *SLS* Bermondsey 1848; Camberwell 1832-3, 1835 (part), Rotherhithe 1865; Southwark 1839, 1862.
Tottenham, North Div., *1918-48. BL* 1937-8, 1947-8; *LMA* 1922-39.
Tottenham, South Div., *1918-48. BL* 1937-8, 1947-8; *LMA* 1922-39.
Tower Hamlets, *1832-85* (thereafter see London). *BL* St George in the East only 1839; *LMA* 1833-54, 1856-65, 1873-85; *HA* Hackney only c.1834, 1841; Shoreditch only 1843, 1845.
THL Bethnal Green 1865; Poplar 1833, 1835, 1849; Whitechapel 1875.
Twickenham, *1945>. BL* 1947>.
Wembley, North Div., *1945>. BL* 1947>.
Wembley, South Div., *1945>. BL* 1947>.
Westminster, *1832-85* (thereafter see London).
BL None; *GL* St Martin in the Fields: 1834, 1851; *LMA* 1839-40, 1844, 1850-1, 1858, 1864-5, 1873-1885; St Clement Danes, St Mary le Strand, St Mary le Savoy and the Liberty of Rolls and Precinct of the Savoy 1840; St Martin in the Fields 1849; *CWA* 1857-9, 1862, 1864-5, 1883; St Margaret only 1868 (owners & proxies only).
Willesden, East Div. *1918>. BL* 1937-8, 1947>.
Willesden, West Div. *1918>. BL* 1937-8, 1947>.

Monmouthshire – *see with* **Wales**, page 57.

36

NORFOLK

Abbreviations
BL = British Library.
GL = Guildhall Library, London.
NHC = Norfolk Heritage Centre, Norfolk & Norwich
Millennium Library, Norwich.
Holdings are virtually the same as for NRO.
NRO = Norfolk Record Office, Norwich.
SoG = Society of Genealogists.
TNA = The National Archives.

County Constituencies

1832-67
Norfolk, Eastern Div. *BL* 1859, 1862-3, 1867;
NHC/NRO 1845-67; *SoG* 1836 (property in Great
Yarmouth); *GL* 1844; *TNA* 1832.
Norfolk, Western Div. *BL* 1859-62; *NHC/NRO* 1845-
1867; *GL* 1844, 1846; *TNA* 1832.

1867-85
Norfolk, North East Div. *BL* 1868-85;
NHC/NRO 1868-1915; *TNA* 1874.
Norfolk, South East Div. *BL* 1868-85;
NHC/NRO 1868-1915; *TNA* 1874.
Norfolk, West Div. *BL* 1868-85; *NHC/NRO* 1868-
1915; *TNA* 1874.

1885-1918
Eastern Div. *BL* 1885/6-1915; *NHC/NRO* 1885-1915;
SoG 1885.
Mid Div. *BL* 1885/6-1915; *NHC/NRO* 1885-1915;
SoG 1885.
Northern Div. *BL* 1885/6-1915; *NHC/NRO* 1885-
1915; *SoG* 1885.
North Western Div. *BL* 1885/6-1915;
NHC/NRO 1885-1915; *SoG* 1885.
Southern Div. *BL* 1885/6-1915; *NHC/NRO* 1885-
1915; *SoG* 1885.
South Western Div. *BL* 1885/6-1915;
NHC/NRO 1885-1915; *SoG* 1885.

1918-48
Eastern Div. *BL* 1918-31, 1937-8, 1947-8;
NHC/NRO 1918-39, 1945-8.
King's Lynn Div. *BL* 1918-31, 1937-8, 1947-8;
NHC/NRO 1918-39, 1945-8.
Northern Div. *BL* 1918-31, 1937-8, 1947-8;
NHC/NRO 1918-39, 1945-8.
Eastern Div. *BL* 1918-31, 1937-8, 1947-8;
NHC/NRO 1918-39, 1945-8.
Southern Div. *BL* 1918-31, 1937-8, 1947-8;
NHC/NRO 1918-39, 1945-8.
South Western Div. *BL* 1918-31, 1937-8, 1947-8;
NHC/NRO 1918-39, 1945-8.

Borough Constituencies
King's Lynn, *1832-1918.* *BL* 1885/6-87;
NHC/NRO 1834-42 (MS); '1920-1'[?];
King's Lynn Lib 1836, 1847-8, 1850-2, 1855-1915,
1921-27, 1929-38; 1947 (part); 1948>.

Norwich, *1832-1948.* *BL* 1832, 1835 (both with polls);
1901-2; 1937-8, 1947-8; *NHC/NRO* 1920-39, 1945-8;
SoG 1832, 1835; 1857 (with poll);
GL 1832, 1857, 1859 (with polls added);
University of Manchester Lib. 1835 (with poll).
Thetford, *1832-1918.* *BL* 1862; *NHC* ?
Great Yarmouth, *1832-67, 1885-1948.* *BL* 1852-3,
1859-63, 1885/6-1915, 1918-30, 1937-8, 1947-8;
NHC/NRO 1832-7, 1843-4, 1846-53, 1855-6, 1858-
1859, 1885-1913, 1915[?]; *NRO* 1919, 1921-6,
1928-30, 1932-3, 1937-9; *GL* 1836, 1839, n.d.,
1844-6, 1851-2;
Great Yarmouth Central Lib 1850, 1914; 1919
(AVL only); 1923, 1932, 1937-38;

Burgess Rolls etc.
King's Lynn. *NHC/NRO* 1835-47, 1849-57, 1865-71,
1876-1915; *King's Lynn Lib* 1899, 1902-12, 1914.
Norwich. 'citizens' lists' *NHC* ?
Great Yarmouth. *NHC/NRO* 1835-6, 1838-42, 1847-8,
1850, 1852-94 (joint from 1895); *GL* 1835-6, 1844.

Freemen
Norwich. *NHC* ?
Great Yarmouth. *Great Yarmouh Lib* 1429-1800
(pubd., 1910).

Overseers' List
King's Lynn. *King's Lynn Lib* 1915.

Post-1948 ER holdings at *BL, NHC, NHC/NRO.*
and *Great Yarmouth* and *King's Lynn Libraries.*

NORTHAMPTONSHIRE
Including the Soke of Peterborough.

Abbreviations
BL = British Library.
GL = Guildhall Library, London.
NLH = Northampton Local History Library.
NRO = Northamptonshire Record Office,
Northampton.
TNA = The National Archives.

County Constituencies

1832-85
Northamptonshire, Northern Div. *BL* 1832, 1841-85;
NRO 1833-85 (except 1869);
NLH 1836, 1839, 1849; *TNA* 1874.
Northamptonshire, Southern Div. *BL* 1841-85;
NRO 1833-85; *NLH* 1833-4, 1836-47, 1852, 1856;
1864 (with index); *TNA* 1874.

1885-1918
Eastern Div. *BL* 1885/6-1915; *NRO* 1886-1915.
Mid Div. *BL* 1885/6-1915; *NRO* 1886-1915.
Northern Div. *BL* 1885/6-1915; *NRO* 1886-1915.
Southern Div. *BL* 1885/6-1915; *NRO* 1886-1915.

Northamptonshire: *County Constituencies* contd.

1918-48
Daventry Div. *BL* 1918-31, 1937-8, 1947-8;
  NRO 1918-39, 1945-8.
Kettering Div. *BL* 1918-31, 1937-8, 1947-8;
  NRO 1918-39, 1945-8.
Peterborough Div. *BL* 1918-31, 1937-8, 1947-8;
  NRO 1918-39, 1945-8;
  Peterborough Central Library **(Archives)** City of
  Peterborough 1932, Soke of Peterborough 1933-9,
  Peterbough Rural District 1946.
Wellingborough Div. *BL* 1918-31, 1937-8, 1947-8;
  NRO 1918-39, 1945-8.

Borough Constituencies
Banbury, *1832-85* (Oxon., but including suburb of
  Grimsbury, in Northants.) – see under Oxfordshire.
Northampton, *1832>.* *BL* 1832, 1854, 1860-3,
  1885/6-1898, 1937-8, 1947>;
  NRO 1834, 1841, 1859-60, 1865-6, 1870-3, 1875-
  1880, 1882-1915, 1918-39, 1945>;
  NLH 1884, 1886, 1892, 1901, 1903-5, 1907-14,
  1919, 1926, 1929-30, 1932-9; *GL* 1832-4.
Peterborough, *1832-1918.* *BL* 1854, 1858-68/9,
  1885/6; *NRO* 1851; *TNA* 1875.
Stamford, *1832-85* – see under Lincolnshire.

Burgess Rolls
Northampton. *NRO* 1832-33, 1849, 1851, 1853,
  1855, 1857, 1859-61, 1863-7, 1869-72, 1874-5,
  1877-1914.

Post-1948 ER holdings at *BL, PCL, NLH, NRO,* and
Corby and *Peterborough Libraries.*

NORTHUMBERLAND

Abbreviations
BL = British Library.
BRO = Berwick upon Tweed Record Office.
GL = Guildhall Library, London.
NCS = Northumberland Collections Service,
           Ashington.
NTL = Newcastle upon Tyne Central Library.
TNA = The National Archives.
TWA = Tyne & Wear Archives Service, Newcastle
           upon Tyne.

County Constituencies
1832-85
Northumberland, Northern Div. *BL* 1835-9, 1843-55,
  1857-64, 1866-74; *NCS* 1832-85; *NTL* 1840;
  GL 1832, 1834-5, 1838; *TNA* 1874.
Northumberland, Southern Div. *BL* 1832, 1835-9,
  1841, 1843-75; *NCS* 1832-85; *NTL* 1840;
  GL 1832, 1834-5, 1837-8, 1840; *TNA* 1874.

Northumberland continued

1885-1918
Berwick upon Tweed Div. *BL* 1885/6; *NCS* 1885-
  1915; *NTL* 1886, 1888, 1891-2, 1904.
Hexham Div. *BL* 1885/6; *NCS* 1885-1915;
  NTL 1891-2, 1904.
Tyneside Div. *BL* 1885/6; *NCS* 1885-1915;
  NTL 1887-8, 1891-2, 1904.
Wansbeck Div. *BL* 1885/6; *NCS* 1885-1915;
  NTL 1886, 1891-2, 1904.

1918-48
Berwick upon Tweed Div. *BL* 1937-8, 1947-8;
  NCS 1918-39, 1945-8.
Hexham Div. *BL* 1937-8, 1947-8;
  NCS 1918-39, 1945-8.
Wansbeck Div. *BL* 1937-8, 1947-8.
  NCS 1918-39, 1945-8.

Borough Constituencies
Berwick upon Tweed, *1832-85.* *BL* 1862-85;
  BRO 1832, 1837-8, 1843-85, 1919;
  NTL 1832; *TNA* 1875.
Morpeth, *1832-48.* *BL* 1937-8, 1947-8;
  NCS 1862-1908.
Newcastle upon Tyne, *1832-1918.* *BL* 1840, 1844-5,
  1847-9, 1852, 1855-7, 1859, 1863, 1885/6, 1888-
  1890, 1893-1905, 1907; *TWA* 1835-59, 1865-74;
  NTL 1832, 1834-9, 1847-8, 1851, 1853-8, 1864,
  1867-8, 1870, 1872, 1877, 1880-1914; *GL* 1833-6.
Newcastle upon Tyne, Central Div., *1918>.*
  BL 1920-1931, 1937-8, 1947>; *NTL* 1918-39,
  1945>; *TWA* 1920-39 (AVL only).
Newcastle upon Tyne, East Div., *1918>.* *BL* 1920-
  1931, 1937-8, 1947>; *NTL* 1918-39, 1945>;
  TWA 1920-39 (AVL only).
Newcastle upon Tyne, North Div., *1918>.*
  BL 1920-1931, 1937-8, 1947>; *NTL* 1918-39,
  1945>; *TWA* 1920-39 (AVL only);
Newcastle upon Tyne, West Div., *1918>.* *BL* 1920-
  1931, 1937-8, 1947>; *NTL* 1918-39, 1945>;
  TWA 1920-39 (AVL only).
Tynemouth, *1832>.* *BL* 1937-8, 1947>; *GL* 1866.
Wallsend, *1918>.* *BL* 1937-8, 1947>.

Burgess Rolls
Berwick upon Tweed. *BL* 1817, 1870/71, 1876/77,
  1906; *BRO* 1796, 1835-36 (North, Middle and South
  Wards, MS); 1846-1912.
Morpeth. *NCS* 1899-1900.
Newcastle upon Tyne. *BL* 1835 (and Ward List).

Freemen
Newcastle upon Tyne. *NTL* 17th and 18th centuries
  (pubd., 2 vols., 1923, 1926).

County Council
NCS 1885-1915.

Some post-1948 ER holdings at *BL* (all), *NTL, NCS,
TWA,* and *Morpeth Central Library.*

NOTTINGHAMSHIRE

County Constituencies

1832-85
Nottinghamshire, Northern Div. *BL* 1846-85;
NA 1839-76, 1878-80, 1882-5; *TNA* 1874.
Nottinghamshire, Southern Div. *BL* 1846-85;
NA 1839-76, 1878-80, 1882-5; *TNA* 1874;
Nottingham Lib 1851; *SoG* 1851 (with poll).

1885-1918
Bassetlaw Div. *BL* 1885/6, 1888-1907; *UN* 188;
NA 1885-1915.
Mansfield Div. *BL* 1885/6, 1888-1907; *NA* 1885-1915;
UN 1887; *Mansfield Lib* 1885.
Newark Div. *BL* 1885/6-1907; *NA* 1885-1915; *UN* 1887;
Newark Lib (MF) 1886-9, 1891-1912, 1914.
Rushcliffe Div. *BL* 1885/6-1907; *NA* 1885-1915;
UN 1887.

1918-48
Bassetlaw Div. *BL* Aut. 1921-31, 1937-8, 1947-8;
NA 1918-39, 1945-8.
Broxtowe Div. *BL* Aut. 1921-31, 1937-8, 1947-8;
NA 1918-39, 1945-8.
Mansfield Div. *BL* Aut. 1921-31, 1937-8, 1947-8;
NA 1918-39, 1945-8; *Mansfield Lib* 1921, 1925-39.
Newark Div. *BL* Aut. 1921-31, 1937-8, 1947-8;
NA 1918-39, 1945-8; *Newark Lib* (MF) 1920-39,
1946-8; Newark incl.. Balderton, Farndon, Hawton &
West Newark (Tolney Green area) 1934;
Newark now also incl. Coddington & Winthorpe 1939.
Rushcliffe Div. *BL* Aut. 1921-31, 1937-8, 1947-8;
NA 1918-39, 1945-8.

Borough Constituencies
Newark upon Trent, *1832-85*. *BL* 1843-63;
Newark Lib 1832-4, 1836-40, 1844, 1846, 1851,
1864, 1868; *TNA* 1873.
Nottingham, *1832-85*. *BL* 1864-6; *NA* 1832-55, 1871,
1876-85; *UN* 1841; *GL* 1837 (St. Nicholas and
St. Peter only); 1840, 1882.
Nottingham, Central Div., *1918>*. *BL* 1918-31, 1937-
1938, 1947>; *NA* 1931-9. 1945>.
Nottingham, East Div., *1885>*. *BL* 1885/6, 1918-31,
1937-8, 1947>; *NA* 1885-1915, 1931-9, 1945>;
UN 1887.
Nottingham, South Div., *1885>*. *BL* 1885/6, 1918-31,
1937-8, 1947>; *NA* 1885-1915, 1931-9, 1945>.
Nottingham, West Div., *1885-1948*. *BL* 1885/6, 1918-
1931, 1937-8, 1947-8; *NA* 1885-1915, 1931-9, 1945>.
East Retford, *1832-85*. *BL* 1864-5; *NA* 1833, 1870-7,
1879, 1885; *GL* 1834, 1880; *TNA* 1872, 1874;
Nottingham Lib Worksop only 1859, 1870, 1880.

Burgess Rolls
Newark. *Newark Lib* 1835, 1839-43, 1866-7, 1895
(incl. qualifying women), 1898-9 (both incl. qualifying
women; 1889 also lists inns, yards, in relation to
roads); 1907, 1911, 1912 (all incl. qualifying women).
Nottingham. *NA* 1835-6, 1874-1915;
UN 1688-1700; 1835, 1837 (Sherwood Ward only);
1854; *Derby Library* 1780; *SoG* 1784, 1846.

Poor Law Union Electoral Registers
County [?] *NA* 1906-15.

Freeholders
County. *UN* 1767 (Chaddesden only) [DrE 33/18].
County Northern. *SoG* 1832.
Nottingham. *SoG* 1784, 1846.

Publications
See *Nottinghamshire F.H.S. Bulletin* **2**.1, **4**.10, both for
Nottingham electoral registers and burgess rolls.

Post-1948 ER holdings at *BL*, *NA*, and *Nottingham*
and *Mansfield Libraries*.

OXFORDSHIRE

County Constituencies

1832-85
Oxfordshire. *BL* 1848, 1851, 1856-85;
ORO 1832-85; *TNA* 1874.
1885 published on microfiche by Oxfordshire FHS.

1885-1918
Mid Div. *BL* 1885/6-91, 1893-1915;
ORO 1885/6-8, 1890-1915..
Northern Div. *BL* 1885/6-91, 1893-1908, 1911-15;
ORO 1885/6-7, 1890-1915.
Southern Div. *BL* 1885/6-91, 1893-1915;
ORO 1885/6-7, 1890-1915;

1918-1948
Banbury Div. *BL* 1918-31, 1937-8, 1947-8;
ORO 1918-38, 1945-8; *CBS* 1927, 1930, 1939.
Henley Div. *BL* 1918-31, 1937-8, 1947-8;
ORO 1918-38, 1945-8.

Oxfordshire continued

Borough Constituencies

Banbury, *1832-85*. BL 1849-68/9, 1871, 1875, 1877-1880; ***CBS*** 1835-45, 1849, 1864.
ER for Banbury (incl. Neithrop) 1865 (also showing 1859 poll) republished by the Open University *(D.301, Social Sciences third level course: Historical Data and the Social Sciences, 1974)*. This was made from a copy in Banbury Library in 1974, but the original now appears to be missing. Copies of the reprint at *ORO* and *SoG*.

Oxford, *1832>. BL* 1885/8, 1937-8, 1947>;
ORO 1832; 1834 (copy),1841-1915, 1918 (incl. AVL) -1939, 1945>.

(New) Woodstock, *1832-85*. BL None; ***TNA*** 1873.

Burgess Rolls, Freemen

Banbury. *ORO* Burgess rolls 1554-1835 (gaps), freemen 1554 (published 1554-1693 in J.S.W. Gibson & E.R.C. Brinkworth, *Banbury Corporation Records, Tudor and Stuart*, Banbury Hist. Soc. **15** (1987); ***CBS*** Burgess rolls 1835, 1868.

Oxford. *ORO* Burgess rolls: 1843-1913 (MS 1837, 1841-51, 1853-56, 1863, 1873-74); freemen: 1832-1889.

University Register

Oxford.*1832-1948*. *BL* 1918-39, 1946.

Post-1948 ER holdings at *BL*, *ORO*, and *Reading Central Library* (South Oxon, Henley).

RUTLAND

Abbreviations
BL = British Library.
LA = Lincolnshire Archives, Lincoln.
TNA = Public Record Office.

County Constituencies

1832-85
Rutlandshire. *BL* 1842-83; ***TNA*** 1874.

1885-1918
Rutlandshire. *BL* 1885-8, 1892-4, 1897-1900.

1918-48
Rutland and Stamford Div. (Pts Kesteven, Lincs.; Rutland Administrative County).
BL Aut. 1921-31, 1937-8, 1947-8;
LA 1919-39, 1945-8 (also AVL 1918-26, 1929, 1931-1932, 1934-9);
Stamford Town Hall possible holdings.

Post-1948 ER holdings at *BL*, *LA* and *The Record Office for Leicestershire, Leicester and Rutland*.

SHROPSHIRE

Abbreviations
BL = British Library.
GL = Guildhall Library, London.
OTC = Oswestry Town Council Records, Powis Hall, Oswestry.
SA = Shropshire Archives.
SoG = Society of Genealogists.
TNA = The National Archives, Library.
Note. ERs formerly in the Local Studies Library are now merged with Shropshire Archives.

County Constituencies

1832-85
Shropshire, Northern Div. *BL* 1842-58, 1860-71;
SA 1832-3, 1835, 1859, 1864, 1873, 1876, 1878-1881, 1883, 1885; *OTC* 1832 (Oswestry only); *TNA* 1874.

Shropshire, Southern Div. *BL* 1842-71;
SA 1832-3, 1836, 1861-2, 1864, 1876, 1879-81, 1883, 1885; *TNA* 1874.

1885-1918
Mid or Wellington Div. *BL* 1885/6;
SA 1886, 1890, 1896, 1900, 1904, 1910.

Northern or Newport Div. *BL* 1885/6;
SA 1886, 1890, 1896, 1900, 1904, 1910, 1915.

Southern or Ludlow Div. *BL* 1885/6;
SA 1886, 1890, 1900, 1904, 1910.

Western or Oswestry Div. *BL* 1885/6;
SA 1886, 1890, 1896, 1900, 1904, 1910, 1915.

1918-48
Ludlow Div. *BL* 1937-8, 1947-8;
SA 1918-39, 1945-8.

Oswestry Div. *BL* 1937-8, 1947-8;
SA 1918-39, 1945-8.
OTC 1934 (Oswestry South Ward only).

Shrewsbury Div. *BL* 1937-8, 1947-8;
SA 1918-39, 1945-8.

The Wrekin Div. *BL* 1937-8, 1947-8;
SA 1918-39, 1945-8.

Borough Constituencies

Bridgnorth, *1832-85*. *BL* 1862-3;
SA 1832, 1836-85(?), 1867, 1874, 1880, 1886 (?);
SoG 1835.

Ludlow, *1832-85*. *BL* None;
SA 1848 (and others, n.d., MS).

Shrewsbury, *1832-1918*. *BL* 1858-63;
SA 1832, 1834-5, 1838, 1840, 1846, 1851;
SoG 1835; *TNA* 1874.

(Much) Wenlock, *1832-85*. *BL* None;
SA 1838, 1857; *SoG* 1835; *GL* 1835; *TNA* 1874.

Burgess Rolls, Freemen

Bridgnorth. *SA* burgess rolls *c*.1657-*c*.1931.

Oswestry. *OTC* burgess rolls: East Ward 1859-70, 1888, 1894, 1899; West Ward 1859-69, 1888, 1894, 1899; North, South, Central and Castle Wards 1899; Castle, North, East and South Wards 1899-1915, 1918-1923; Central and West Wards 1899-1915, 1918-24; freemen: 1696-1908; honorary freemen: 1893-1971.

Shropshire: *Burgess Rolls* continued

Shrewsbury. *Shrewsbury Burgess Roll* 13th century to 1924, published index, ed. H.E. Forrest (1924). Index to a further 16th-17th century roll and current roll, 1925-35, published in *Transactions of Shropshire Arch. Soc.* **48** (1934-5). Original records still held by *Shrewsbury and Atcham Borough Council*, The Guildhall, Dogpole, Shrewsbury. *SA* Canvasser's list: 1822 (MS).

County Council Electors
Oswestry. *OTC* 1900.

Post-1948 ER holdings at *BL* and *SA*.

SOMERSET

Abbreviations

BL	=	British Library.
BRL	=	Bath Reference Library.
BRO	=	Bath & North East Somerset Record Office.
GL	=	Guildhall Library, London.
SAS	=	Somerset Archive & Record Service, Taunton.
SoG	=	Society of Genealogists.
TNA	=	The National Archives, Library.
WsM	=	Weston super Mare, Woodspring Central Library.

County Constituencies

1832-67
Somersetshire, Eastern Div. *BL* None;
 SAS 1832-1867; *BRL* 1835 (Bath only);
 WsM 1837-9, 1846-7, 1850-1867 (?Weston only);
 GL 1832, 1846; *SoG* 1833.
Somersetshire, Western Div. *BL* 1860;
 SAS 1832-1867; *Exeter Central Lib.* 1832;
 SoG 1833; *GL* 1832, 1834-5, 1846.

1867-85
Somersetshire, East Div. *BL* None; *SAS* 1867-85;
 WsM 186774, 1876-84 (?Weston only); *TNA* 1874.
Somersetshire, Mid Div. *BL* None; *SAS* 1867-85;
 TNA 1874.
Somersetshire, West Div. *BL* None; *SAS* 1867-85.

1885-1918
Bridgwater Div. *BL* None; *SAS* 1885-1915.
Eastern Div. *BL* None; *SAS* 1885-1915.
Frome Div. *BL* None; *SAS* 1885-1915.
Northern Div. *BL* None; *SAS* 1885-1915.
Southern Div. *BL* None; *SAS* 1885-1915.
Wells Div. *BL* None; *SAS* 1885-1915;
 WsM 1885-6 (?Weston only); *SoG* 1891.
Western or **Wellington Div.** *BL* None;
 SAS 1885-1915; *SoG* 1904.

Somerset continued

1918-48
Bridgwater Div. *BL* 1937-8, 1947-8;
 SAS 1918-39, 1945-8.
Frome Div. *BL* 1937-8, 1947-8; *SAS* 1918-39, 1945-8.
Taunton Div. *BL* 1937-8, 1947-8;
 SAS 1918-39, 1945-8.
Wells Div. *BL* 1937-8, 1947-8; *SAS* 1918-39, 1945-8.
Weston-super-Mare Div. *BL* 1937-8, 1947-8;
 SAS 1918-39, 1945-8.
Yeovil Div. *BL* 1937-8, 1947-8; *SAS* 1918-39, 1945-8.

Borough Constituencies
Bath, 1832>. *BL* 1844-8, 1850-67, 1872, 1881-1915, 1918-31, 1937-8, 1947>; *BRO* 1832-1914, 1918-39, 1945>; *BRL* 1909-15, 1918-39 (1918-9 incl. AVL), 1945, 1948-54; *Bristol Central Lib.* 1851, 1885.
Bridgwater, 1832-67. *BL* 1865-6;
 SAS 1935-46, 1868-70;
Bristol, 1832-95. *BL* 1832, 1864, 1866-84;
Bristol, South Div., 1885-1918. *BL* None;
Frome, 1832-85. *BL* 1845, 1855-62, 1865, 1867-1868/9.
Taunton, 1832-1918. *BL* 1885/6;
 Taunton Local History Lib 1832 & 1834 (MS, with voting intentions); 1840-1, 1864.
Wells, 1832-67. *BL* None;

Burgess/Citizens' Rolls
Bath. *BL* 1885-86-1914/15; *BRL* 1897.

Freeholders
County. *GL* 1733.

Post-1948 ER holdings at BL, BRL, BRO, SAS and Bristol Central Lib.

STAFFORDSHIRE

Abbreviations
BL   = British Library.
BLC   = Burton Local & Family History Centre.
DAS   = Dudley Archives & L.H. Service.
GL   = Guildhall Library, London.
LRO   = Lichfield Record Office.
SDL   = Stourbridge District library
SL   = Stafford Library.
SRO   = Staffordshire Record Office, Stafford.
STCA = Stoke-on-Trent City Archives.
TNA   = The National Archives, Library.
WLHC = Walsall Local History Centre.
WoA   = Wolverhampton Archives & Local Studies.

County Constituencies

1832-67

Staffordshire, Northern Div. *BL* None; *SRO* 1832-67 (excl. Pirehill, Totmanslow Hds 1836); *LRO and BLC* 1832-67 Offlow North Hd, east Staffs as relevant [mf]; *STCA* 1832-67 Pirehill, Totmanslow Hds (excl.1836), north Staffs as relevant [mf];
Birmingham Central Lib 1836, 1838-42, 1861.
Staffordshire, Southern Div. *BL* 1851; *SRO* 1832-67 (excl. Offlow South Hd 1832, Cuttleston West 1834); *LRO* 1832-67 Offlow South (excl. 1832), East Staffs as relevant [mf]; *SDL* Sedgley c.1850;
Birmingham Central Lib 1838-42.

1868-85

Staffordshire, East Div. *BL* None; *TNA* 1874; *SRO* 1868-85 (1882 missing);
BRL Handsworth and Perry Bar, 1874-85.
Staffordshire, North Div. *BL* None; *TNA* 1874; *GL* 1832-35, 1837-42, 1844-45, 1848-1849, 1851 (incomplete),1856, 1861; *SRO* 1868-85 (1882 missing); *STCA* 1868-85 (1882 missing) [mf].
Staffordshire, West Div. *BL* None; *TNA* 1874; *GL* 1833, 1835, 1837-49, 1861; *SRO* 1868-85 (1882 missing); *LRO and BLC* 1868-85 (1882 missing) [mf]; *SDL* Coseley 1911; Sedgley 1870, 1874; *DAS* Coseley, 1872.

1885-1918

Burton Div. *BL* None; *SRO* 1885-88, 1891-1908; *LRO and BLC* 1885-88, 1891 [mf].
Handsworth Div. *BL* None; *SRO* 1885-88, 1891-1908; *BRL* Handsworth and Perry Bar, 1885-88.
Kingswinford Div. *BL* None; *SRO* 1885-88, 1891-1908.
Leek Div. *BL* None; *SRO* 1885-88, 1891-1908; *STCA* 1885-88, 1891 [mf].
Lichfield Div. *BL* None; *SRO* 1885-88, 1891-1908; *LRO* 1885-88, 1891 [mf].
North Western Div. *BL* None; *SRO* 1885-88, 1891-1908; *STCA* 1885-88, 1891 [mf].
Western Div. *BL* None; *SRO* 1885-88, 1891-1908; *DAS* Sedgley 1928-39, 1947-49; *SDL* Coseley 1911..

1918-48

Burton Div. *BL* 1937-38, 1947-48; *SRO* 1918-39, 1945-48.
Cannock Div. *BL* 1937-38, 1947-48; *SRO* 1918-39, 1946-48.
Kingswinford Div. *BL* 1937-38, 1947-48; *SRO* 1918-1939, 1945-48; *Brierley Hill Lib* Brierley Hill 1938-39, 1945>; *Stourbridge District Lib* Amblecote, 1938.
Leek Div. *BL* 1937-38, 1947-48, 1947-48; *SRO* 1918-1939, 1945-48.
Lichfield Div. *BL* 1937-38, 1947-48; *SRO* 1918-39, 1945-48; *Lichfield Lib* 1924, Lichfield Rural District 1931, 1936.
Stafford Div. *BL* 1937-38, 1947-48; *SRO* 1918-39, 1945-48; *SL* 1946>.
Stone Div. *BL* 1937-38, 1947-48; *SRO* 1918-39, 1945-1948.

Borough Constituencies

Dudley, *1832>.* *BL* 1885/86, 1937-38; 1947>; *DAS* 1894-1915, 1918-39, 1947>; Sedgley 1947>.
Hanley (and Burslem), *1885-1918.* *BL* 1885/86-1915; *STCA* 1885/86-1915 [mf].
Lichfield, *1832-1885.* *BL* None; *LRO* 1832-41 (also 1837 MS); *SRO* 1840, 1844.
Newcastle-under-Lyme, *1832-1885.* *GL* 1832; *Newcastle Lib* 1840, 1845 (copies); 1878, 1933; *TNA* 1873.
Newcastle-under-Lyme (incl. Tunstall), *1885>* *BL* 1885/86, 1937-1938; 1947>; *STCA* 1910; East ward only: 1909, 1912.
Smethwick, *1918>.* *BL* 1937-38, 1947>.
Stafford, *1832-1918.* *BL* 1885/86, 1894; *TNA* 1874; *SRO* 1832, 1834-36; 1838, 1840-41, 1843, 1852, 1854, 1857-61, 1865, 1868, 1872 (incomplete); *SL* 1857, 1860-61, 1865.
Stoke-upon-Trent, *1832-1885* (Burslem, Fenton, Hanley, Longton, Stoke, Tunstall). *BL* 1856-63; *STCA* 1857-63 [MF]; *TNA* 1871-72.
Stoke-upon-Trent, *1885-1918* *BL* 1911-15; *STCA* Longton ward: 1899-1906/7; Stoke wards: 1903/4, 1909-10; whole constituency 1911-15 [mf], 1915 [orig.]. *See also* Hanley, Newcastle *above.*
Stoke-on-Trent, Burslem Div. (incl. Tunstall) *1918-1948.* *BL* 1937-1938, 1947-48; *STCA* 1918-0, 1926-1939, 1945-48.
Stoke-on-Trent, Hanley Div. *1918-48.* *BL* 1937-38, 1947-48; *STCA* 1918-9, 1922-3, 1926-39, 1945-48.
Stoke-on-Trent, Stoke Div. (incl. Fenton, Longton) *1918-48.* *BL* 1937-38, 1947-48; *STCA* 1918-9, 1922, 1925-39, 1945-48.
Tamworth (part in Warw. until 1866), *1832-85.* *TNA* 1871-72.
Walsall, *1832>.* *BL* 1864-1915, 1937-38; 1947>; *WLHC* 1832-35, 1837-40, 1846-50, 1856-1915 (missing 1867, 1883, 1897, 1905), 1918-39, 1945>; Rushall 1877; *TNA* 1874.
Wednesbury, *1868>.* *BL* 1887-1904, 1906-08, 1910-1913, 1915, 1937-38; 1947>; *TNA* 1874; *WLHC* Darlaston 1931, 1938-39, 1947-48.

Staffordshire: *Borough Constituencies* continued

Wolverhampton, *1832-85*. BL 1860-67, 1871-85;
TNA 1874; *WoA* Bilston 1871, 1874-77; Sedgley
1875-76, (Coseley only) 1910; Wednesfield and
Heath Town 1870, 1874-76; Willenhall 1870, 1872,
1875; Wolverhampton 1852, 1857, 1861-63, 1867,
1870-71, 1873-74, 1877-80.
Wolverhampton, Bilston Div. *1918-48*.
BL 1937-38, 1947-48; *WoA* 1938-39, 1945-48.
Wolverhampton, East Div. *1885-1948*.
BL 1885/86-1899, 1902-15, 1937-38;
WoA Heath Town 1910, Wednesfield and Heath
Town 1926; Willenhall 1910, 1926; Wolverhampton
1926, 1930, 1933-39, 1945-1948.
Wolverhampton, South Div. *1885-1918*.
BL 1885/86-1899, 1902-15;
Wolverhampton, West Div. *1885-1948*. BL 1885/86-
1899, 1902-15, 1937-38; *WoA* Wolverhampton
1926, 1930, 1933-39, 1945-1948.

Burgess Rolls etc.
Dudley. *DAS* 1865, 1893-1915.
Lichfield. *LRO* 1835-53, 1856-57 (some omissions).
Newcastle-under-Lyme. *Newcastle Museum* 1620-
1792, 1734-1830, 1790, 1807-18, 1838, 1877, 1832-
1884; *SRO* 1827-37 [mf].
Stafford. *SL* 1822; *SRO* 1694-1837; ward list for
municipal elections 1835, 1838, 1840, 1845, 1850,
1855-66.
Walsall. *WLHC* 1835-40, 1848-50, 1852, 1877, 1883.

Freemen
Lichfield. *LRO*: Freemen rolls, ten companies, C17-
C18; 1799-1831 (some companies omitted); 1835-
1846; *SRO* Voters and freemen entitled to vote for
Lichfield City constituency 1832..
Newcastle-under-Lyme. *Newcastle Lib* 1890-1914
(East and West Wards); *Newcastle Museum*
admissions 1620-1906, copy orders 1590-1790;
SRO mf of these admissions and copy orders.
Stafford. *SRO* 1788-1875.

*Post-1948 ER holdings at SRO, DAS, LRO, STCA,
WLHC, WoA, Brierley Hill, Newcastle-under-Lyme,
Stourbridge District, and Tamworth Libraries,*

SUFFOLK
Abbreviations
BL = British Library.
SRO(B) = Suffolk Record Office, Bury St Edmunds.
SRO(I) = Suffolk Record Office, Ipswich.
SRO(L) = Suffolk Record Office, Lowestoft.
TNA = The National Archives, Library.

County Constituencies
1832-85
Suffolk, Eastern Div. BL 1850-85; *TNA* 1873, 1875;
SRO(I) 1843-49, 1860-1, 1866, 1870, 1874-80.
Suffolk, Western Div. BL 1850-85; *TNA* 1874;
SRO(I) 1866; *SRO(B)* 1832-72, 1882.

1885-1918
North-Eastern or Eye Div. BL 1885/6-94, 1896-98;
SRO(I) 1898.
North-Western or Stowmarket Div. BL 1885/6-94,
1896-98, 1902-15; *SRO(I)* 1898; *SRO(B)* 1889-
1915.
Northern or Lowestoft Div. BL 1885/6-94, 1896-98;
SRO(L) 1889, 1898.
South-Eastern or Woodbridge Div. BL 1885/6-94,
1896-98; *SRO(I)* 1898.
Southern or Sudbury Div. BL 1885/6-94, 1896-98,
1902-15; *SRO(B)* 1885-1915.

1918-1948
East Suffolk:
Eye Div. BL 1937-38, 1947-48; *SRO(I)* 1920-38.
Lowestoft Div. BL 1937-38, 1947-48;
SRO(L) 1920-38.
Woodbridge Div. BL 1937-38, 1947-48;
SRO(I) 1920-1938, 1945>.

West Suffolk:
Bury St Edmunds Div. BL 1937-38, 1947-48.
Sudbury Div. BL 1937-38, 1947-48.

Borough Constituencies
Bury St Edmunds, *1832-1918*. BL 1861-63, 1885;
SRO(B) 1837-39, 1842-44, 1855-59, 1889-1915,
1918-39, 1945>.
Eye, *1832-85*. BL 1843-63; *TNA* 1875.
Ipswich, *1832>*. BL 1839-43, 1851-63, 1871, 1885/86,
1897, 1937-38, 1947>; **SRO(I)** 1875, 1877-80, 1882-
1885, 1887-8, 1890-1, 1893-1915, 1918-39, 1945>.
Sudbury, *1832-85* (or *1844*). BL None;
SRO(B) 1840 (copy).
Thetford – *see* Norfolk.
Great Yarmouth – *see* Norfolk.

Burgess Rolls etc.
Beccles. *SRO(L)* 1834-60, 1877-1913.
Ipswich. *SRO(I)* 1835, 1840-49; 1850, 1861 (both
incomplete); 1871, 1875; 1876 (incomplete); 1877-
1880; 1881 (incomplete); 1882-85, 1887-91, 1893-
1915.
Southwold. *SRO(L)* 1835-77, 1888, 1896.

*Post-1948 ER holdings at BL, SRO(I), SRO(B), SRO
(Lowestoft).*

SURREY

For the metropolitan area, see also under London: *BL, Lambeth, Merton, Morden* and *Southwark Libraries*.

Abbreviations
BL = British Library.
CCL = Croydon Central Library.
GL = Guildhall Library, London.
LA = Lambeth Archives Dept., Minet Library,
MES = Morden Electoral Services Office, Crom House, London Road, Morden SM4 5DX
RRL = Richmond Reference Library.
SHC = Surrey History Centre, Woking.
SLS = Southwark Local Studies Library, 211 Borough High Street, SE1.
SoG = Society of Genealogists.
TNA = The National Archives, Library.

County Constituencies

1832-67

Surrey, Eastern Div. *BL* 1859, 1861-64; *GL* 1864; *SHC* 1832-68 (missing 1833, 1867); *LA* Streatham 1832, 1841-2, 1850; claimants 1832, 1838-9, 1841-2, 1847, 1850; *Mitcham Library* Mitcham 1832-39?
Surrey, Western Div. *BL* 1859, 1862-65; *CCL* 1851; *SHC* 1832-68 (missing 1833, 1867); *SoG* Epsom 1866.

1868-85

East Surrey, East Surrey Div. *BL* 1870-72; *TNA* 1872; *SHC* 1869-85; *SoG* Clapham 1872; *LA* Lambeth 1872.
East Surrey, Mid Surrey Div. *BL* 1868/9; *TNA* 1872 *SHC* 1869-85.
Surrey, Western Div. *BL* 1870-71, 1873; *TNA* 1872; *SHC* 1869-85.

1885-1918

Surrey, Kingston Div. *BL* 1885/86-1915; *SHC* 1885-1918; *RRL* Barnes U.D. 1913.
Mid Surrey or **Epsom Div.** *BL* 1887-1915; *SHC* 1885-1918.
North-Eastern Surrey or **Wimbledon Div.** *BL* 1885/86-89, 1891-1915; *SHC* 1885-1918. *Merton Central Library* 1891-98, Wimbledon 1903, 1906, 1908-9; *Mitcham Library*; Mitcham 1891-98; *Morden Library* Merton and Morden 1891-98.
North-Western Surrey or **Chertsey Div.** *BL* 1887-1915; 1885-1918.
South-Eastern Surrey or **Reigate Div.** *BL* 1887-1915; *SHC* 1885-1918.
South-Western Surrey or **Guildford Div.** *BL* 1887-1915; *SHC* 1885-1918.

1918-48

Carshalton Div., *1945-58*. *BL* 1947-48; *SHC* 1918-39, 1945-48.
Chertsey Div. *BL* 1937-38, 1947-48; *SHC* 1918-39, 1945-48.
Eastern Surrey Div. *BL* 1937-38, 1947-48; *SHC* 1918-39, 1945-48.

Epsom Div. *BL* 1937-38, 1947-48; *SHC* 1918-39, 1945-48.
Farnham Div. *BL* 1937-38, 1947-48; *SHC* 1918-39, 1945-48.
Guildford Div. *BL* 1937-38, 1947-48; *SHC* 1918-39, 1945-48.
Mitcham Div. *BL* 1937-38, 1947-48; *SHC* 1918-39, 1945-48. *Morden Library* Merton and Morden, 1936-9, 1945>; *MES* Mitcham 1931-9, 1945>.
Reigate Div. *BL* 1937-38, 1947-48; *SHC* 1918-39, 1945-48.

Borough Constituencies

Croydon, *1885-1918*. *BL* 1885/86; *CCL* 1883[sic]-1915.
Croydon, North, *1918>*. *BL* 1937-38, 1947>; *CCL* 1918-39, 1945>.
Croydon, South, *1918-48*. *BL* 1937-38, 1947-48; *CCL* 1918-39, 1945-48.
Guildford, *1832-85*. *BL* None; *TNA* 1873; *SHC* 1832-1843 (MS), 1851, 1856-7, 1859, 1864-6, 1883-4.
Kingston-upon-Thames, *1918>*. *BL* 1937-38, 1947>; *Kingston Borough Archives*. 1918>[?].
Lambeth, *1832-85* (*thereafter see* London). *BL* None; *LA* Lambeth 1832-87 *[sic]* (incl.St Giles Camberwell and St Mary Newington).
Newington, Walworth Div. *See under* London.
Reigate, *1832-85*. *BL* 1854-55, 1863.
Richmond, *1918>*. *BL* 1937-38, 1947-48; *RRL* Richmond and Barnes 1918-40, 1945>.
Southwark, *1832-85* (*thereafter see under* London). *BL* None; *SLS* Bermondsey 1848; Camberwell 1832-1833, 1835 (part); Rotherhithe 1865; Southwark 1839, 1862.
Wandsworth. *See under* London.
Wimbledon, *1918>*. *BL* 1937-38, 1947>; *Merton Central Lib* 1938-9, 1946>; *MES* 1927-39, 1945>.

Burgess Rolls

Richmond Borough. *RRL* 1902-14.
Wimbledon. *Merton Central Lib* 1906, 1910.

Freemen

Guildford. *SHC* 1655-1933. (pubd., ed. H. Carter, 1963).

Post-1948 holdings at BL; SHC; Electoral Registration Dept., Guildhall, Kingston; CCL, Mitcham Library, MES, RRL.

SUSSEX

Abbreviations
BL = British Library.
ESRO = East Sussex Record Office, Lewes.
GL = Guildhall Library, London.
SoG = Society of Genealogists.
TNA = The National Archives, Library.
WDL = Worthing Divisional Library.
WSRO = West Sussex Record Office, Chichester.

County Constituencies

1832-85
Sussex, Eastern Div. *BL* 1837, 1859, 1861-64, 1870-1872; *GL* 1832, 1837 (both with polls added); 1841, 1856; *SoG* 1832 (with votes), 1837; *TNA* 1874; *ESRO* 1832, 1841-66, 1868, 1870-85; *WDL* 1837.
Sussex, Western Div. *BL* 1838, 1841-53, 1855-85; *GL* 1841; *TNA* 1874; *WSRO* 1832, 1835, 1838, 1842-85; *WDL* 1864.

1885-1918
Eastern Sussex or Rye Div. *BL* 1885/86-1915; *ESRO* 1888-90, 1892-95; 1885, 1887-1915 ??

Mid Sussex or Lewes Div. *BL* 1885/86-1915; *ESRO* 1887-1915; *WDL* Worthing only 1905, 1909, 1914.
Northern or East Grinstead Div. *BL* 1885/86-1915; *ESRO* 1885, 1887-1915;
North-Western or Horsham Div. *BL* 1885/86-1913; *WSRO* 1890-1915;
Southern or Eastbourne Div. *BL* 1885/86-1915; *ESRO* 1885, 1887-1915;
South-Western or Chichester Div. *BL* 1885/86-1913; *WSRO* 1885-89, 1890-1915.

1918-1948
East Sussex:
Eastbourne Div. *BL* 1937-38, 1947-48; *ESRO* 1918-1939, 1945-48.
East Grinstead Div. *BL* 1937-38, 1947-48.
Lewes Div. *BL* 1937-38, 1947-48; *ESRO* 1918-39, 1945-48.
Rye Div. *BL* 1937-38, 1947-48; *ESRO* 1918-39, 1945-1948.

West Sussex:
Chichester Div. *BL* 1937-38, 1947-48; *WSRO* 1918-1939, 1945-48.
Horsham Div. *1945-48. BL* 1947-48; *WSRO* 1945-48;
Horsham and Worthing Div., *1918-45. BL* 1937-38; *WSRO* 1918-39;
Worthing Div., *1945-48. BL* 1947-48; *WSRO* 1945-48; *WDL* 1924-5, 1927-39, 1945-48.

Borough Constituencies
Arundel, *1832-67. BL* None;
Brighton, *1832-1948. BL* 1855, 1862-65, 1868-1913, 1915, 1918-31, 1937-38, 1947-48; *GL* 1834, 1836, 1840-41, 1846, 1851, 1853; *Brighton Reference Lib* 1831[sic], 1855-1915, 1918-36, 1945-48; Hove 1929, 1931, 1945-1948; *Hove Central Lib* Hove 1892-97, 1899-1912, 1914, 1926-1939, 1945-48.

Chichester, *1832-85. BL* None; *TNA* 1874; *WSRO* 1833-45, 1868, 1883-1914 [Chichester City Archives: BW, BX].
Hastings, *1832-1918, 1918>. BL* 1854, 1862-63, 1885/6-1901, 1903-15, 1918-31, 1937-38, 1947>; *ESRO* 1835-97; *Hastings Central Lib* 1836 (copy), 1928-39, 1945>. St Clement's parish, 1840 (copy), St Mary Magdalen and other parishes, n.d. (copy).
Horsham, *1832-85. BL* None; *GL* 1840-41, 1847, 1849, 1852-54, 1856, 1858, 1863-64, 1866-69; 1870 (with MS additions); 1872-73, 1876; *TNA* 1873.
Lewes, *1832-85. BL* 1849-63; *ESRO* 1885; *SoG* 1835.
Midhurst, *1832-85. BL* No ne; *TNA* 1871.
Rye, *1832-85. BL* None; *TNA* 1874; *WDL* 1852 (with poll added).
(New) Shoreham, *1832-85. BL* None; *TNA* 1871; *WDL* 1836; n.d. (*c.*1850 MS); 1856, 1858, 1876, 1875-80 (part). Cowfold only 1836, 1841, 1856.

Burgess Rolls
Brighton. *Brighton Reference Lib* 1854-1915.
Chichester. *WSRO* 1833-45, 1868, 1883-1914 [Chichester City Archives: Bw, BX].

Post-1948 holdings at BL; ESO, WSRO; Bexhill, Brighton, Hastings, Hove and *Worthing Libraries.*

WARWICKSHIRE

Abbreviations
BCL = Birmingham Central Library, Local Studies and History Section.
BL = British Library.
CCL = Coventry Central Library.
CRO = Coventry Record Office.
LSL = Leamington Spa Library.
SLA = Shakespeare Centre Library & Archive
SCL = Sutton Coldfield Central Library.
TNA = The National Archives, Library.
WL = Warwick Library.
WRO = Warwickshire County Record Office, Warwick

County Constituencies

1832-85
Warwickshire, Northern Div. *BL* 1858-85; *BCL* 1836, 1868, 1885; *CCL* Foleshill 1832-33; *SCL* Sutton Coldfield 1851; *WRO* 1832-36, 1838-1885; Ryton-on-Dunsmore 1885;
Warwickshire, Southern Div. *BL* 1858-85; *BCL* 1872, 1876 (£50 voters only); *SLA* 1865, 1867; 1869 (incomplete); Stratford-upon-Avon 1832-34; *see also* burgess rolls; *WRO* 1832-55, 1857-85 (incl. political affiliations of £50 voters in 1878); Bidford 1874-75; Fenny Compton 1842; Kenilworth n.d. (C19);

1885-1918
Northern Warwickshire (or Tamworth) Div. *BL* 1885/6-1915; 1886-1905, 1907-15; *BCL* 1888 (Birmingham voters only); Sutton Coldfield n.d. (*c.*1847); 1852; *WRO* ??; Kineton 1915;

Warwickshire: *County 1885-1918* continued

North-Eastern Warwickshire (or Nuneaton) Div.
BL 1885/6-1915; *WRO* 1886-1905, 1907-15; Astley, parochial register 1894;

South-Eastern Warwickshire (or Rugby) Div.
BL 1885/6-1915; *WRO* 1886-1905, 1907-15; Ryton-on-Dunsmore 1885;

South-Western Warwickshire (or Stratford on Avon) Div. *BL* 1885/6-1915; *WRO* 1886-1905, 1907-1915;

1918-48

Warwickshire, Nuneaton Div. *BL* 1918-31, 1937-38, 1947-48; *Nuneaton Library* 1921-39, 1945-48; *WRO* 1920-39, 1945-48;

**Warwickshire, Rugby Div., *1918-45*. *BL* 1918-31, 1937-38; *WRO* 1920-39.

**Warwickshire, Rugby Div., *1945-48*. *BL* 1947-48; *WRO* 1945-48.

**Warwickshire, Solihull Div., *1945-48*. *BL* 1947-48; *WRO* 1945-48.

**Warwickshire, Sutton Coldfield Div., *1945-48*. *BL* 1947-48; *SCL* 1945-48; *WRO* 1945-48.

**Warwickshire, Tamworth Div., *1918-45*. *BL* 1918-Spr. 1923, 1924-31, 1937-38; *SCL* Sutton Coldfield 1918-39; *WRO* 1920-39, 1945.

**Warwickshire, Warwick and Leamington Div., *1918-45*. *BL* 1918-Spr. 1923, 1924-31, 1937-38; *WL* 1932-33, 1935-39; *WRO* 1920-39; Stratford R.D. 1938.

**Warwickshire, Warwick and Leamington Div., *1945-48*. *BL* 1947-48; *LSL* Leamington Spa 1918-1920, 1923, 1926-38; *WL* 1947; *WRO* 1945-48.

Borough Constituencies

**Aston Manor, *1885-1918*. *BL* 1885/86, 1896; *BCL* 1885-6, 1888-94, 1896-7, 1899-1915 (1912 Lozells Ward only); Erdington parish 1911.

**Birmingham, *1832-85*. *BL* 1859-64; *BCL* 1839-85;

Birmingham. The *'Birmingham Electoral Roll'* for **1912, 1920, 1925, 1930** and **1935**, and the AVL for **1918** have been scanned by Tony Abrahams to produce an index of around 2,500,000 names. This can be viewed on a pay-per-view basis on website <www.midlandshistoricaldata.org> or free of charge from public access PCs in participating libraries.

**Birmingham, Acock's Green, *1945-48*. *BL* 1947-48.

**Birmingham, Aston, *1918-48*. *BL* Aut. 1921-31, 1937-1938, 1947-48; *BCL* 1918-38, 1945-48.

**Birmingham, Bordesley, *1885-1918*. *BL* 1885/86, 1897; *BCL* 1885-1915.

**Birmingham, Central, *1885-1918*. *BL* 1885/86, 1897; *BCL* 1885-1915.

**Birmingham, Deritend, *1918-48*. *BL* Aut. 1921-31, 1937-38, 1947-48; *BCL* 1918-39, 1945-48.

**Birmingham, Duddleston, *1918-48*. *BL* Aut. 1921-31, 1937-38, 1947-48; *BCL* 1918-39, 1945-48.

**Birmingham, East, *1885-1918*. *BL* 1885/86, 1897; *BCL* 1885-1915.

**Birmingham, Edgbaston, *1885-1918*. *BL* 1885/86, 1897; *BCL* 1885-1915.

**Birmingham, Edgbaston, *1918>*. *BL* Aut. 1921-31, 1937-38, 1947>; *BCL* 1918-39, 1945>.

**Birmingham, Erdington, *1918>*. *BL* Aut. 1921-31, 1937-38, 1947>; *BCL* 1918-39, 1945>.

**Birmingham, Handsworth, *1918>*. *BL* 1918> ??; *BCL* 1918-39, 1945>.

**Birmingham, King's Norton, *1918-48*. *BL* Aut. 1921-1931, 1937-1938, 1947-48; *BCL* 1918-39, 1945-48.

**Birmingham, Ladywood, *1918>*. *BL* Aut. 1921-31, 1937-38, 1947>; *BCL* 1918-39, 1945>.

**Birmingham, Moseley, *1918-45*. *BL* Aut. 1921-31, 1937-38; *BCL* 1918-39, 1945>.

**Birmingham, Moseley, *1945-48*. *BL* 1947-48; *BCL* 1945-48.

**Birmingham, North, *1885-1918*. *BL* 1885/86, 1897; *BCL* 1885-1915.

**Birmingham, South, *1918-48*. *BL* 2885/86, 1897; *BCL* 1918-39, 1945-48.

**Birmingham, Sparkbrook, *1918-48*. *BL* Aut. 1921-31, 1937-38, 1947-48; *BCL* 1918-39, 1945-48.

**Birmingham, West, *1885-1918*. *BL* 1885/86, 1897; *BCL* 1885-1915.

**Birmingham, West Birmingham, *1918-48*. *BL* Aut. 1921-31, 1937-38, 1947-48; *BCL* 1918-39, 1945-48.

**Birmingham, Yardley, *1918-48*. *BL* Aut. 1921-31, 1937-38, 1947; *BCL* 1918-39, 1945-48.

**Coventry, *1832-1918*. *BL* 1858, 1860, 1862-65, 1885-1915; *TNA* 1874; *CCL* 1834, 1858, 1877-1915.

**Coventry, *1918-45*. *BL* 1918-Spr. 1919, Spr. 1920, 1931, 1937-38; *CCL* 1918-39; *CRO* 1933-39; *WRO* 1931.

**Coventry, East, *1945-48*. *BL* 1947-48; *CCL* 1945-48; *CRO* 1945-48.

**Coventry, West, *1945-48*. *BL* 1947-48; *CCL* 1945-48; *CRO* 1945-48.

**Warwick, *1832-85*. *BL* None; *WL* 1833; *WRO* 1832-1860, 1879-85; Warwick Borough 1880-82 MS.

**Warwick and Leamington, *1885-1918*. *BL* None; *WRO* 1885-1915.

Burgess Rolls

Birmingham. *BCL* 1838-42, 1848, 1864, 1866-1914.

Coventry. *CCL* 1836 (parishes of Stoke, Wyken and Foleshill only); 1855, 1857, 1877.

Leamington Spa. *LSL* 1874, 1876, 1881-90, 1892-7, 1899-190, 1902-13; *WRO* 1893.

Stratford-upon-Avon. *SLA* 1836-1914, 1920-35, 1938.

Sutton Coldfield. *BCL* 1906, 1910-15; *SCL* 1918-39.

Warwick. *WRO* 1835, 1841, 1845, 1847-48, 1850-61; *WL:* (St Mary's) 1853, 1875.

Overseers' Lists etc.

Northern and **Southern Warwickshire.** *WRO* Overseers' lists: 1832-96; Warwick Borough (C19).

Birmingham. *BCL* Ownership electors, 1901-4, 1906-1914; electors of Guardians 1894-1906.

Leamington Spa. *LSL* parochial registers 1905, 1909, 1912-15; jury lists 1905, 1907, 1912-14, 1916-17.

Some post-1948 ER holdings at *BL* (all), *BCL, CCL, LSL, Nuneaton Library, Solihull Central Library, SCL, WL, WRO,*

WESTMORLAND
Now part of Cumbria

Abbreviations
BL = British Library.
CRO = Cumbria Record Office, Kendal.
GL = Guildhall Library, London.
SoG = Society of Genealogists.
TNA = The National Archives, Library.

County Constituencies
1832-85
Westmorland. *BL* None; *TNA* 1872, 'County, North 1873, 1875', 'County, South 1874'; *CRO* 1832-85; *GL* 1832; *SoG* 1832.

1885-1918
Westmorland, Northern or **Appleby Div.** *BL* 1885/6, 1891-1915; *CRO* 1885-1915.
Westmorland, Southern or **Kendal Div.** *BL* 1900, 1902, 1906, 1909, 1911; *CRO* 1885-1915.

1918-48
Westmorland. *BL* 1937-38, 1947-48; *CRO* 1918-1939, 1945-48 (incl. service voters).

Borough Constituency
Kendal, *1832-85.* *BL* 1860-63.

Burgess Rolls
Appleby and **Kendal.** *CRO* 1888-1914.

Some post-1948 ER holdings at *BL* (all), *CRO*.

WILTSHIRE

Abbreviations
BL = British Library.
GL = Guildhall Library, London.
SoG = Society of Genealogists.
TNA = The National Archives, Library.
WAS = Wiltshire Archaeological & Natural History Society, Devizes.
WSA = Wiltshire & Swindon Archives, Chippenham.

County Constituencies
1832-85
Wiltshire, Northern Div. *BL* 1861-85; *WSA* 1832-85; *WAS* 1833, 1840-43, 1851, 1857, 1864.
Wiltshire, Southern Div. *BL* 1860-85; *TNA* 1874; *WSA* 1832-85; *WAS* 1833, 1840-43, 1848.

1885-1918
Wiltshire, Eastern or **Devizes Div.** *BL* 1885/6-1915; *WSA* 1885-1915.
Wiltshire, Northern or **Cricklade Div.** *BL* 1885/6-1915; *WSA* 1885-1915.
Wiltshire, North-Western or **Chippenham Div.** *BL* 1885/6-1915; *WSA* 1885-1915.
Wiltshire, Southern or **Wilton Div.** *BL* 1885/6-1915; *WSA* 1885-1915.
Wiltshire, Western or **Westbury Div.** *BL* 1885/6-1915; *WSA* 1885-1915.

Wiltshire continued

1918-48
Wiltshire, Chippenham Div. *BL* 1937-38, 1947-48; *WSA* 1918-39, 1945-48.
Wiltshire, Devizes Div. *BL* 1937-38, 1947-48; *WSA* 1918-39, 1945-48.
Wiltshire, Salisbury Div. *BL* 1937-38, 1947-48; *WSA* 1918-39, 1945-48.
Wiltshire, Swindon Div. *BL* 1937-38, 1947-48; *WSA* 1918-39, 1945-48.
Wiltshire, Westbury Div. *BL* 1937-38, 1947-48; *WSA* 1918-39, 1945-48.

Borough Constituencies
Calne, *1832-85.* *BL* None; *TNA* 1875; *WSA* 1835-84.
Chippenham, *1832-85.* *BL* 1863-66, 1868; *TNA* 1875; *WSA* 1836-81.
Cricklade, *1832-85.* *BL* 1852-53, 1861-64; *TNA* 1873 (incl. Swindon and many other places); *WSA* 1858-1860; *GL* 1837 (MS, with canvass and poll).
Devizes, *1832-85.* *BL* 1845-55, 1857, 1859-73, 1877, 1880-85; *WSA* 1838, 1844-64.
Malmesbury, *1832-85.* *BL* 1854, 1863-64; *TNA* 1872.
Marlborough, *1832-85.* *BL* 1832-65, 1868/69-1872, 1878-85; *WSA* 1834-84.
Salisbury, *1832-1918.* *BL* 1832, 1854, 1885/86, 1889; *TNA* ('New Sarum') 1832.
Westbury, *1832-85.* *BL* 1857-61, 1863-65; *TNA* 1874; **Wilton, *1832-85.*** *BL* 1854, 1860-63, 1866, 1885; *TNA* 1874; *WSA* 1849-63.

Burgess Rolls, Freemen
Marlborough. *SoG* 1869 (burgess rolls); *TNA* 1854 (freemen).

Post-1948 ER holdings at *BL* (all), *WSA* (all).

WORCESTERSHIRE

Abbreviations
BL = British Library.
BCL = Birmingham Central Library, Local Studies and History Section.
SLA = Shakespeare Centre Library & Archive
SoG = Society of Genealogists.
TNA = The National Archives, Library.
WRO = Worcestershire County Record Office.

County Constituencies
1832-1885
Worcestershire, Eastern Division. *BL* 1863; *TNA* 1874; *WRO* 1843-85; *BCL* 1847-1862; *SLA* 1881 (Inkberrow only).
Worcestershire, Western Division, 1832-85. *BL* 1859, 1863; *TNA* 1874; *WRO* 1843-85, Wolverley only 1837.

Worcestershire: County Constituencies continued

1885-1918

Worcestershire, Eastern Division. *BL* 1885/6; *WRO* 1885-1915.

Worcestershire, Mid or **Droitwich Division.** *BL* 1885/6; *WRO* 1843-1915.

Worcestershire, Northern Division. *BL* 1885/6; *WRO* 1843-1915.

Worcestershire, Southern or **Evesham Division.** *BL* 1885/6; *WRO* 1843-1915.

Worcestershire, Western or **Bewdley Division.** *BL* 1885-6; *WRO* 1843-1915.

1918-1948

Worcestershire, Bewdley Div. *BL* 1937-8, 1947-8; *WRO* 1918-39, 1945-48.

Worcestershire, Evesham Div. *BL* 1937-8, 1947-8; *WRO* 1918-39, 1945-48.

Worcestershire, Kidderminster Div. *BL* 1937-8, 1947-8; *WRO* 1918-39, 1945-48; *Kidderminster Central Library* 1934, 1936, 1838, 1945-48.

Worcestershire, Stourbridge Div. *BL* 1937-1938, 1947-8; *WRO* 1918-39, 1945-48.

Borough Constituencies

Bewdley, *1832-85.* *BL* none; *WRO* 1843-85 **[?]**; *BCL* 1837-8, 1840, 1844-6, 1851.

Evesham, *1832-85.* *BL* 1854, 1863-66, 1867; *WRO* 1843-85 [?]; *SLA* 1868.

Kidderminster, *1832-1918.* *BL* 1863, 1897; *WRO* 1843-1915, ?1918 **[?]**; *Kidderminster Central Library* 1849.

City of Worcester, *1832-1948.* *BL* 1843-45, 1847-1850, 1852-64, 1868/9-92, 1895-1915, 1937-38, 1947-48; *WRO* 1843-99 **[?]**; *SoG* 1934.

Burgess rolls

Evesham. *WRO* 1826, 1832, 1834, 1836, 1851, 1864.

Some post-1948 ER holdings at *BL* (all), *KL*, *WRO*.

YORKSHIRE

City of YORK

(not associated with any Riding)

Abbreviations
BL = British Library.
GL = Guildhall Library, London.
TNA = The National Archives, Library.
YCA = York City Archives (some names missing because of damage; some registers and rolls available only as photocopies).
YLS = York Local Studies Collection.

Borough Constituency

City of York, *1832-1918.* *BL* 1832, 1847-65, 1868/69; *TNA* 1873, 1874; *YLS* 1832, 1835-37, 1839-57, 1859-70, 1874-76, 1878-79, 1881-1915; *GL* 1834, 1878.

York, *1918>.* *BL* 1937-38, 1947>; *YLS* 1918-39 (incl. AVL 1918, 1920-24), 1945>.

Yorkshire: *City of York* continued

Burgess rolls

York. *YCA* 1835-42, 1847, 1862-69, 1872-78, 1886-1915.

Freemen

York. *YLS* 1272-1847; 1847-date (MF, original at York Guildhall); 1272-1759 pubd. in Surtees Soc., **96, 102** (1897, 1900); 1760-1835 pubd. by Robert Davies (1835). From 1760, freemen's claims give further details, incl. birth or baptism certs. for those claiming freedom by birthright; *BL* 1835.

Parochial Registers

York. *YCA* 1894-1914.

Some post-1948 ER holdings at *BL* (all), *YCA*, *YLS* (all).

YORKSHIRE: EAST RIDING

Abbreviations
BL = British Library.
ERY = East Riding of Yorkshire Archives and Local Studies Service, Beverley.
GL = Guildhall Library, London.
HCA = Hull City Archives (there is also a collection of other material relating to voting).
HCL = Hull Central Library.
TNA = The National Archives, Library.

County Constituencies

1832-1867

Yorkshire, East Riding Div. *BL* 1863-67; *ERY* 1832-1867 (1833 MS); *HCL* 1834-36, 1855; *GL* 1836.

1868-1885

East Riding of Yorkshire. *BL* 1868-85; *TNA* 1874; *ERY* 1868-72, 1874-85; *HCL* 1871, 1874; *GL* 1868, 1873.

1885-1918

East Riding, Buckrose Div. *BL* 1885/86,-1915; *ERY* 1885-1915; *Bridlington Library* 1899-1912.

East Riding, Holderness Div. *BL* 1885/86,-1915; *ERY* 1885-1915; *HCL* 1895.

East Riding, Howdenshire Div. *BL* 1885/86; *ERY* 1885-1915; *HCL* 1905.

1918-1948

East Riding, Buckrose Div. *BL* 1937-38, 1947-48; *ERY* 1918-39, 1945-48; *Bridlington Library* 1899-1912

East Riding, Holderness Div. *BL* 1931 (incomplete), 1937-38, 1947-48; *ERY* 1918-39, 1945-48.

East Riding, Howdenshire Div. *BL* 1937-38, 1947-1948; *ERY* 1918-39, 1945-48;

Yorkshire: East Riding continued

Borough Constituencies

Beverley, *1832-1870*. BL 1846-47, 1850-55, 1857-66, 1868/69-70; *ERY* 1832, 1834-68 (also MS 1835, 1837 [DDBC/11]); *HCA* 1832; *HCL* 1840.

Kingston upon Hull, *1832-1885*. BL 1835; *HCA* 1843-1885; *HCL* 1832-72, 1874-76, 1878-85.

Kingston upon Hull, Central Div. *1885>*. **BL** 1885/86-1915, Aut. 1920-31, 1937-38, 1947>; *HCA* 1885-1915; 1918-39, 1945>; *HCL* 1885-1915, 1918-39, 1945>.

Kingston upon Hull, East Div. *1885>*. **BL** 1885/86-1915, Aut. 1920-31, 1937-38, 1947>; *HCA* 1885-1915; 1918-39, 1945>; *HCL* 1885-1915, 1918-39, 1945>.

Kingston upon Hull, North-West Div. *1918-48*. **BL** Aut. 1920-31, 1937-38, 1947-48; *HCA* 1918-39, 1945>; *HCL* 1918-39, 1945-48.

Kingston upon Hull, South-West Div. *1918-48*. **BL** Aut. 1920-31, 1937-38, 1947-48; *HCA* 1918-39, 1945>; *HCL* 1918-39, 1945-48.

Kingston upon Hull, West Div. *1885-1918*. **BL** 1885/86-1915; *HCA* 1885-1915; *HCL* 1885-1915.

Malton (Norton) (mostly North Riding), *1832-85*. **BL** None.

Burgess Rolls

Beverley. *ERY* 1710-1836 (MS) [BC.IV/7/4-20]; 1835-1844, 1846-48, 1850, 1852-53, 1855-69 (incomplete, some contain only one ward only: 1838-39, 1853 MS) [DDBC/11].

Hedon (Burgess Admissions) *ERY* 1752-1890 [DDHE/9/5,7,8]; (Burgess Rolls) 1860-87, 1913 [some MSS; DDHE/9/9-11].

Kingston-upon-Hull. *HCA* 1835-1914 (almost complete), merged with Parliamentary register in 1918.

Freemen

Beverley. *ERY* 1755-date [BC/IV/7].

Kingston-upon-Hull. *HCA* 1369-1885; *BL* 1835.

Some post-1948 ER holdings at *BL* (all), *ERY*, *HCA*, *HCL*.

YORKSHIRE: NORTH RIDING

Abbreviations

BL	=	British Library.
GL	=	Guildhall Library, London.
MCL	=	Middlesbrough Central Library.
NYC	=	North Yorkshire County Record Office, Northallerton.
SoG	=	Society of Genealogists.
TA	=	Teesside Archives, Middlesbrough.
TNA	=	The National Archives, Library.

County Constituencies

1832-1885

Yorkshire, North Riding Div. BL 1861; *TNA* 1874; *NYC* 1832-75; *GL* 1834; *SoG* Out-voters 1865; *MCL* 1841 (Middlesbrough property owners only); 1869-78 (Redcar, Eston Marton, Thornaby only).

1885-1918

North Riding, Cleveland Div. BL None.

North Riding, Richmond Div. BL None.

North Riding, Thirsk and Malton Div. BL None.

North Riding, Whitby Div. BL None.

1918-1948

North Riding, Cleveland Div. BL 1937-38, 1947-48; *NYC* 1920, 1925, 1930-33, 1936.

North Riding, Richmond Div. BL 1937-38, 1947-48; *NYC* 1920, 1925, 1930-33, 1936.

North Riding, Scarborough and Whitby Div. BL 1937-38, 1947-48; *NYC* 1931.

North Riding, Thirsk and Malton Div. BL 1937-38, 1947-48; *NYC* 1920, 1925, 1930-33, 1936.

Borough Constituencies

Malton (partly East Riding), *1832-85*. **BL** None.

Middlesbrough, *1867-1918*. BL None; *TA* 1868-69, 1872-74, 1876-1914, 1918 (incl. AVL).

Middlesbrough, East, *1918>*. BL 1837-38, 1947>; *TA* 1918 (incl. AVL), 1919-39, 1945>.

Middlesbrough, West, *1918>*. BL 1937-38, 1947>; *TA* 1918 (incl. AVL), 1919-39, 1945>.

Northallerton, *1832-85*. BL 1857, 1859-64, 1870, 1872-73, 1876-77, 1880-82, 1884.

Richmond, *1832-85*. BL None.

Stockton-on-Tees, *1868>*. BL 1885/86, 1889-1915, 1937-38, 1947>.

Thirsk, *1832-85*. BL None.

Whitby, *1832-85*. BL 1844-50, 1852-57, 1859-83.

Burgess Rolls

Middlesbrough. *TA* 1852-62 (MS); 1866, 1869-74, 1876, 1879-1914; *MCL* 1868 (various townships).

Some post-1948 ER holdings at *BL* (all), *MCL*, *NYC*.

YORKSHIRE: WEST RIDING

Abbreviations

BAL	=	Barnsley Archive & Local Studies Dept.
BCL	=	Bradford Central Library.
BL	=	British Library.
GL	=	Guildhall Library, London.
HaL	=	Halifax Central Library.
HuL	=	Huddersfield Central Library.
LCL	=	Leeds Central Library.
SCL	=	Sheffield Central Library.
SoG	=	Society of Genealogists.
TNA	=	The National Archives, Library.
WAS	=	Wakefield: West Yorks. Archive Service.
WL	=	Wakefield Library H.Q.

County Constituencies

1832-1862 or 1867

Yorkshire, West Riding Div. *BL* 1832-34, 1836-61; *WAS* 1840-67; *BAL* 1844 (Thurlstone property owners only); *BCL* 1832; *HuL* 1832 (Agrigg and Morley Wapentakes only); *SoG* 1834, 1840; *GL* 1832; 1848 (Barnsley area only, with poll added).

1862-1885

Yorkshire: Northern Div. of the West Riding. *BL* 1862-85; *TNA* 1874; *WAS* 1862-85; *Keighley Library* 1882-8.

Yorkshire: Southern Div. of the West Riding. *BL* 1862-85; *TNA* 1874; *WAS* 1862-85; *BAL* 1874.

1868-1885

Yorkshire: Eastern Div. of the West Riding. *BL* 1868/69-85; *WAS* 1868-85.

1885-1918
West Riding, Eastern Part

Barkston Ash Div. *BL* 1885/6-1915; *WAS* 1885-1915; *Leeds Archives (WYAS)* Seacroft only: 1902, 1905, 1913.

Morley Div. *BL* 1885/6-1915; *WAS* 1885-1915; *Batley Library* 1906.

Otley Div. *BL* 1885/6-1915; *WAS* 1885-1915.

Pudsey Div. *BL* 1885/6-1915; *WAS* 1885-1915.

Ripon Div. *BL* 1885/6-1915; *WAS* 1885-1915.

Spen Valley Div. *BL* 1885/6-1915; *WAS* 1885-1915.

West Riding, Northern Part

Elland Div. *BL* 1885/6-1915; *WAS* 1885-1915; *HaL* 1894 (various districts).

Keighley Div. *BL* 1885/6-1915; *WAS* 1885-1915; *Keighley Library* 1885-1914.

Osgoldcross Div. *BL* 1885/6-1915; *WAS* 1885-1915.

Shipley Div. *BL* 1885/6-1915; *WAS* 1885-1915; *BCL* 1914 (Clayton only).

Skipton Div. *BL* 1885/6-1915; *WAS* 1885-1915.

Sowerby Div. *BL* 1885/6-1915; *WAS* 1885-1915.

West Riding, Southern Part

Barnsley Div. *BL* 1885/6-1915; *WAS* 1885-1915; *BAL* 1915.

Colne Valley Div. *BL* 1885/6-1915; *WAS* 1885-1915.

Doncaster Div. *BL* 1885/6-1915; *WAS* 1885-1915.

Hallamshire Div. *BL* 1885/6-1915; *WAS* 1885-1915.

Holmfirth Div. *BL* 1885/6-1915; *WAS* 1885-1915.

Normanton Div. *BL* 1885/6-1915; *WAS* 1885-1915; *Rotherham Central Library* 1910-15.

1918-1948
West Riding of Yorkshire

Barkston Ash Div. *BL* 1937-38, 1947-48; *WAS* 1918-1939, 1945-48.

Colne Valley Div. *BL* 1937-38, 1947-48; *WAS* 1918-1939, 1945-48.

Don Valley Div. *BL* 1937-38, 1947-48; *WAS* 1918-39, 1945-48.

Doncaster Div. *BL* 1937-38, 1947-48; *WAS* 1918-39, 1945-48.

Elland Div. *BL* 1937-38, 1947-48; *WAS* 1918-39, 1945-48; *HaL* 1918 (Southowram only).

Hemsworth Div. *BL* 1937-38, 1947-48; *WAS* 1918-39, 1945-48.

Keighley Div. *BL* 1937-38, 1947-48; *WAS* 1918-39, 1945-48; *Keighley Library* 1918-39, 1945-48.

Normanton Div. *BL* 1937-38, 1947-48; *WAS* 1918-39, 1945-48.

Penistone Div. *BL* 1937-38, 1947-48; *WAS* 1918-39, 1945-48.

Pontefract Div. *BL* 1937-38, 1947-48; *WAS* 1918-39, 1945-48.

Pudsey and Otley Div. *BL* 1937-38, 1947-48; *WAS* 1918-39, 1945-48; *LCL* 1935-39, 1945.

Ripon Div. *BL* 1937-38, 1947-48; *WAS* 1918-39, 1945-48.

Rother Valley Div. *BL* 1937-38, 1947-48; *WAS* 1918-1939, 1945-48; *Rotherham Central Lib* 1945-48.

Rothwell Div. *BL* 1937-38, 1947-48; *WAS* 1918-39, 1945-48.

Shipley Div. *BL* 1937-38, 1947-48; *WAS* 1918-39, 1945-48.

Skipton Div. *BL* 1937-38, 1947-48; *WAS* 1918-39, 1945-48.

Sowerby Div. *BL* 1937-38, 1947-48; *WAS* 1918-39, 1945-48.

Spen Valley Div. *BL* 1937-38, 1947-48; *WAS* 1918-39, 1945-48.

Wentworth Div. *BL* 1937-38, 1947-48; *WAS* 1918-39, 1945-48.

Borough Constituencies

Barnsley, *1918>.* *BL* 1937-38, 1947>; *WAS* 1918-20; *BAL* 1918-39 (AVL 1918-26, 1928-31, 1933-39); 1945 (incl. services), 1946>.

Batley and Morley, *1918>.* *BL* 1937-38, 1947>; *Batley Library* 1918-39, 1945>; *HuL* 1918, 1945>; *LCL* 1947>; *WAS* 1918-20.

Bradford, *1832-85.* *BL* None; *WAS* 1840-85; *Bradford Archives (WYAS)* 1832, 1850-1915; *BCL* 1846; 1868 (Great Horton only); 1879-85; *GL* 1868 (with poll added).

Bradford Central, *1885>.* *BL* 1897, 1901-15, Aut. 1919-31, 1937-38, 1947>; *WAS* 1885-1915, 1918-20; *BCL* 1885-1914, 1918-39, 1945>.

Bradford East, *1885>.* *BL* 1897, 1901-15, Aut. 1919-1931, 1937-38, 1947>; *WAS* 1885-1915, 1918-20; *BCL* 1885-1914, 1918-39, 1945>.

Yorkshire, West Riding: *Boroughs* continued

Bradford North, *1918>. BL Aut. 1919-1931, 1937-38, 1947>; *BCL* 1918-39, 1945>; *WAS* 1918-20.
Bradford South, *1918>. BL 1918; *WAS* 1918-20; *BCL* 1918-39, 1945>.
Bradford West, *1885-1918. BL 1897, 1901-15; *WAS* 1885-1915, 1918-20.
Dewsbury, *1867-1918. BL 1885/6. 1888, 1897; *TNA* 1874; *Dewsbury Library* 1874-79, 1881-84, 1892, 1894-95, 1898, 1913; *WAS* 1885-1915; *HuL* 1866-69, 1872-76, 1878-79, 1881-95, 1897, 1910, 1913-15;
Dewsbury, *1918>. BL 1937-38, 1947>; *HuL* 1918; *WAS* 1918-20.
Halifax, *1832-1918. BL 1863, 1885/6, 1897; *HaL* 1832, 1835, 1838, 1848, 1852, 1870, 1872, 1875, 1877, 1889, 1882; *WAS* 1840-1915.
Halifax, *1918>. BL 1937-38, 1947>; *WAS* 1918-20; *HaL* 1921, 1927, 1929, 1931, 1934, 1945>.
Huddersfield, *1832-1918. BL 1885/86, 1888-89, 1892, 1897; *HuL* 1833, 1875, 1897-1904, 1906-14; 1915 (incl. parochial register); *WAS* 1840-1915; *TNA* 1875.
Huddersfield, *1918-48. BL 1937-38, 1947-48; *HuL* 1918-39 (incl. AVL 1918-21, 1926); 1945-48; *WAS* 1918-20.
Knaresborough, *1867-85. BL 1868/69-73; *WAS* 1867-85.
Leeds, *1832-85. BL 1858, 1863-64; *TNA* 1874; *GL* 1860; *LCL* 1832, 1836-1838, 1840, 1846-85; *Leeds Archives (WYAS)* 1833 [AM]; *WAS* 1840-85.
Leeds Central, *1885>. BL 1885/86-88, 1918-Spr. 1919 (incl. AVL), Spr. 1920-31, 1937-38, 1947>; *LCL* 1885-1915, 1918-39, 1945>; *WAS* 1885-1915, 1918-20.
Leeds East, *1885-1948. BL 1885/86-88, AVL 1918-Spr. 1919; *LCL* 1885-1915, 1918-39, 1947-48; *WAS* 1885-1915, 1918-20.
Leeds North, *1885>. BL 1885/86-88, 1918-Spr. 1919 (incl. AVL), Spr. 1920-31, 1937-38, 1947>; *LCL* 1885-1915, 1918-39, 1947>; *WAS* 1885-1915, 1918-20.
Leeds North East, *1918>. BL 1918-Spr. 1919 (incl. AVL), Spr. 1920-31, 1937-38, 1947>; *LCL* 1918-39, 1947>; *WAS* 1918-20.
Leeds South, *1885>. BL 1885/86-88, 1918-Spr. 1919 (incl. AVL), Spr. 1920-31, 1937-38, 1947>; *LCL* 1885-1915, 1918-39, 1947>; *WAS* 1885-1915, 1918-20.
Leeds South East, *1918>. BL 1918-Spr. 1919 (incl. AVL), Spr. 1920-31, 1937-38, 1947>; *LCL* 1918-39, 1947>; *WAS* 1918-20.
Leeds West, *1885>. BL 1885/86-88, 1918-Spr. 1919 (incl. AVL), Spr. 1920-31, 1937-38, 1947>; *LCL* 1885-1915, 1918-39, 1947>; *WAS* 1885-1915, 1918-20.

Pontefract, *1832-1918. BL None; *WAS* 1840-1915; *WL* 1842, 1872 (both on loan).
Ripon, *1832-85. BL 1842-76, 1878-85; *WAS* 1840-85.
Rotherham, *1918>. BL 1937-38, 1947>; *Rotherham Central Library* 1918-39, 1945>; *WAS* 1918-20.
Sheffield, *1832-85. BL None; *SCL* 1861, 1870, 1872, 1874-76, 1880-81; *WAS* 1840-85.
Sheffield, Attercliffe, *1885>. BL 1937-38, 1947>; *SCL* 1885-91, 1899, 1900, 1903, 1907, 1911, 1920-1939, 1945>; *WAS* 1885-1915, 1918-20.
Sheffield, Brightside, *1885>. BL 1937-38, 1947>; *SCL* 1885-91, 1899, 1900, 1903, 1907, 1911, 1920-1939, 1945>; *WAS* 1885-1915, 1918-20.
Sheffield, Central, *1885-1948. BL 1937-38, 1947-48; *SCL* 1885-91, 1899, 1900, 1903, 1907, 1911, 1920-1939, 1945-48; *WAS* 1885-1915, 1918-20.
Sheffield, Eccleshall, *1885-1948. BL 1937-38, 1947-1948; *SCL* 1885-91, 1899, 1900, 1903, 1907, 1911, 1920-39, 1945-48; *WAS* 1885-1915, 1918-20.
Sheffield, Halam, *1885>. BL 1937-38, 1947>; *SCL* 1885-91, 1899, 1900, 1903, 1907, 1911, 1920-1939, 1945>; *WAS* 1885-1915, 1918-20.
Sheffield, Hillsborough, *1918>. BL 1937-38, 1947>; *SCL* 1920-1939, 1945>; *WAS* 1918-20.
Sheffield, Park, *1885>. BL 1937-38, 1947>; *SCL* 1885-91, 1899, 1900, 1903, 1907, 1911, 1920-1939, 1945>; *WAS* 1885-1915, 1918-20.
Wakefield, *1832-1918. BL 1847-63; *WL* 1832-1915; *WAS* 1840-1915.
Wakefield, *1918>. BL 1937-38, 1947>; *TNA* 1874; *WL* 1918-39, 1945>; *WAS* 1918-20.

Burgess Rolls
Barnsley. BAL 1869 (MS); 1871, 1877, 1879-1914.
**Batley. *Batley Library* 1878, 1898.
**Bradford. *BCL* 1848-78; *BL* 1866.
**Dewsbury. *Dewsbury Library* 1862-64, 1867-74, 1876-77, 1879-95, 1897, 1912-14.
**Doncaster. *Doncaster Archives, Balby* 1844-1915 (some MS).
**Wakefield. *WL* 1850-1915 (incomplete).

Parochial Registers
**Bradford. *Bradford Archives (WYAS)* 1896-1909.
**Halifax. *HaL* 1905, 1908-13.
**Huddersfield. *HuL* 1915.

Some post-1948 ER holdings at *BL* (all), *BAL, BCL, HaL, HuL, LCL, SCL, WL, WAS* (West Riding [county] complete 1840-1915, 1918-39, 1945>; [boroughs] 1840-1915, 1918-1920). *Batley, Castleford, Cleckheaton, Doncaster, Ilkley* and *Rotherham Libraries.*

WALES and Monmouthshire

Note. An exhaustive re-examination of Electoral Registers has been made at the *National Library of Wales*. I am most grateful to the considerable trouble gone to by staff, which has greatly enhanced the coverage in this Guide.

ANGLESEY

Abbreviations

ARO = Anglesey County Record Office, Llangefni.
BL = British Library.
NLW = National Library of Wales, Aberystwyth.
TNA = The National Archives, Library.
UWL = University of Wales, Library, Bangor
UWM = University of Wales, Bangor (Dept. of Manuscripts).

County Constituency

1832-85

Anglesey. BL None; **TNA** 1874; **ARO** 1832-34, 1836, 1838-40, 1846, 1848-49, 1851, 1860-1861 (both incomplete), 1862-64, 1867; **UWL** 1836, 1838-39, 1841-42, 1844-47, 1850, 1856, 1860-61; **UWM** 1835 [UCNW.4908]; 1836 [Pen. 1382].

1885-1918

Anglesey. BL 1885/86, 1897; **NLW** 1915;
ARO 1885, 1888-1889; **UWL** 1908, 1910.

1918-1948

Anglesey. BL 1937-38, 1947-48; **NLW** 1918-19, 1921, 1929, 1945, 1947-48; **ARO** 1919, 1921-22, 1925, 1929, 1934-36, 1938-39.

Boroughs Constituency

Beaumaris (with **Amlwch, Holyhead, Llangefni**), *1832-85.* **BL** 1852-56, 1859-60, 1862-65; **TNA** 1870, 1874; **ARO** 1873, 1880; **UWL** 1832, 1834, 1859, 1870-72, 1874; **UWM** 1832 (draft, Holyhead only) [UCNW.29474]; 1832-47 (draft) [BA.II.J.351-70]; 1845 (draft, Beaumaris only) [BA.IV.D.345]; 1847 (draft) [UCNW.29475-61]; 1848-71 (draft) [BA.IV.B.72-94]; 1845-46, 1848, 1851, 1859, 1868 [BA.IV.B.95-103]; 1853 (draft) [UCNW.29477]; 1853-1854 (draft) [BA.II.J.351-370]; 1860-62, 1864-67 (drafts) [BA.I.FB.19-26].

Burgess Rolls

Beaumaris. UWM. 1751-1826, 1835-46, 1848-1853, 1855-63, 1865-70 [BA.IV.115-45]; 1835-51 [BA.I.FB.8], 1851-88 [BA.III.B.29-30]; certs. of election 1694-1832 [BA.II.I.B85-89].

Freeholders (?)

Anglesey. NLW. *c.*1724 [Wynnstay L.791].

Freemen

Beaumaris. UWM. 1792-1833 [BA.I.FB.7]; 1848-71 [BA.IV.B.72-94].

Some post-1948 ER holdings at **BL** (all), **ARO**.

BRECONSHIRE or BRECKNOCKSHIRE
(now in Powys)

Abbreviations

BL = British Library.
GL = Guildhall Library, London.
NLW = National Library of Wales, Aberystwyth.
PAO = Powys County Archives Office, Llandrindod Wells.
TNA = The National Archives, Library.

County Constituency

1832-1885

Brecknockshire. BL None; **TNA** 1871; **NLW** 1835-36 [Maybery 6374, 6447, 6375]; **PAO** 1836-85 [Brecons. Q.S. Q/REe]; **GL** 1832.

1885-1918

Brecknockshire. BL 1885/86-1902; **PAO** 1885-87, 1904, 1906 (all incomplete); 1910-14; **NLW** 1915.

1918-1948

Breconshire and Radnorshire. BL Aut. 1921-32, 1937-38, 1947-48; **NLW** 1918, 1929, 1945.

Borough Constituency

Brecon, *1832-1885*. BL None; **NLW** 1835-37, 1845, 1851-52, 1868, 1870, 1879-80 [Maybery]; **PAO** 1852.

Burgess or freemen lists (?)

Brecon. NLW 1556-1785 [Tredgar Park 120/61]; early 18th century [T Pk 117/179]; 1761, 1763, 1771 [T Pk 120/61, 117/202].

Freeholders (?)

Brecknockshire. NLW early 18th century [Tredegar Park 117/355]; 1787 [Castell Gorfod 64]; *c.*1754 (Crickhowell only) [Badminton 11,798].

Post-1948 ER holdings at **BL** (all).

Cronicle (April 1997) has an article on Registers of Electors, Freeholders and Jurors' Lists in Powys.

CAERNARVONSHIRE (Carnarvonshire)
(now Caernarfon)

Abbreviations
BL = British Library.
CRO = Caernarfon Record Office (Gwynedd Archives & Museums Service), Caernarfon.
NLW = National Library of Wales, Aberystwyth.
TNA = The National Archives, Library.
UWL = University of Wales, Library, Bangor
UWM = University of Wales, Bangor (Dept. of Manuscripts).

County Constituency

1832-1885
Carnarvonshire. BL 1863; **TNA** 1875;
NLW 1632, 1834-36, 1868-69, 1874, 1880;
CRO 1832 (except Pwllheli area); 1833-37, 1840-43, 1847-49, 1851-68, 1870, 1872-1876, 1878, 1880-85;
UWL 1843, 1851-85;
UWM 1832 (draft: Llandudno only) [Mostyn 7855]; *c.*1832 (draft: Llanrhos only) [Mostyn 7866].

1885-1918
Carnarvonshire, Northern or Arfon Div. BL None;
CRO 1885-87, 1889-91; 1892 (except Llanddeirioler and Dionorvic); 1893; 1894 (incomplete); 1895-96; 1898; 1899; 1900, 1901; 1902-03; 1904, 1906 (both incomplete); 1907; 1910 (Aber and Llanllechid only); 1914 (incomplete); 1915; **UWL** 1885/6, 1889-95; **NLW** 1915(?).
Carnarvonshire, Southern or Eifion Div. BL None;
CRO 1885-87, 1889-91; 1892 (except Llanddeirioler and Dionorvic); 1893; 1894 (incomplete); 1895-96; 1897, 1898, 1899 (most); 1900, 1902-03; 1904, 1906 (both incomplete); 1907 (most); 1910 (Aber and Llanllechid only); 1913 (incomplete); 1914 (incomplete); 1915; **UWL** 1885/6, 1889-95; **NLW** 1915(?).

1918-1948
Carnarvonshire. BL 1937-38, 1947-48;
NLW 1918-19, 1929-30, 1932-39, 1945-48.
CRO 1920-39, 1945-48.

Boroughs Constituency
Carnarvon District of Boroughs, 1832-1948
(Bangor, Carnarvon, Conway, Criccieth, Llandudno [from 1918], Llanfairfechan [from 1918], Nevin, Penmawrmawr [from 1918], and Pwllheli).
BL 1857-63, 1937-38, 1947-48; **TNA** 1873-74; **UWL** 1836-41, 1843, 1846, 1850-53, 1858-59, 1864-1865, 1873; **NLW** 1920-27, 1929-30, 1934-39, 1945-1948; **UWM** 1834 (draft) [PA.12594-97]; 1838-1840 (draft, with MS additions) [PC.3722-6].
CRO 1832-44 (MS register for all boroughs); 1847 (Pwllheli only); 1857, 1868, 1882 (Bangor, Caernarvon only); 1883 (Criccieth, Nefyn only); 1884-1885 (Caernarvon, Criccieth, Nefyn only); 1888; 1889 (Caernarvon only); 1890-93 (Caernarvon, Criccieth, Nefyn only); 1894 (Caernarvon only); 1896; 1897 (Caernarvon, Pwllheli only); 1898; 1899 (Caernarvon East Ward only); 1900, 1902-03; 1907 (Conway only); 1915; 1929-39; 1945-48;

Burgess (or Freemen) Rolls
Caernarvon. CRO 1757-1834; **NLW** *c.*1631, 1665-69, 1694-1713 [Llanfair & Bryndol B12, B20, B26-7].
Conway. CRO 1785-1828 (Minutes of election of burgesses) [Conway Borough papers]; 1830 [Poole Papers].
Criccieth. CRO 1783 [XD1/327]; 1830, 1832 [Poole Papers].
Nefyn. CRO 1707-13 [XD2/4223-4], 1756-82 [XD1/328], 1832 [Poole Papers],.
Pwllheli. CRO 1713; **UWM** 1739 [Mostyn 6154]; 1781-1831 [PA.12576]; n.d. [PA.12583]; elections 1708-96 (gaps) [Mostyn 6146-57].

Burgesses' Petition
Boroughs (Pwllheli only?). **UWM** *c.*1784 [Mostyn 7842].

Freeholders
Carnarvonshire, CRO *c.*1722 (Is-wyrfai Hundred only) [XD2/4230]; *c.*1734 (Uchaf Hundred only) [XD2/4234]; **UWM** 1747 (incl. Hundreds of Nant Conwy, Issaph, Uchaf, Creyddin; perhaps others) [Mostyn 7840-41]; n.d. (various Hundreds and Commotes) [PA. 12537-42].

Jury Lists (freeholders)
Carnarvonshire, CRO 1733-49; jurors' books: 1826-1842, 1852-56, 1905, 1911.

Overseers' Returns
Carnarvonshire, CRO 1825-1920. Earlier returns are to be found in the Quarter Sessions rolls.

Some post-1948 ER holdings at **BL** (all), **CRO**.

CARDIGANSHIRE (Ceredigion)

Abbreviations
BL = British Library.
CA = Ceredigion (Cardiganshire) Archives (Archifdy Ceredigion).
GL = Guildhall Library, London.
NLW = National Library of Wales, Aberystwyth.
TNA = The National Archives, Library.

County Constituency

1832-1885
Cardiganshire. BL None; **TNA** 1874; **NLW** 1835-36; 1848, 1856-57,1865-66, 1874; Mid-19th century [Falcondale 77-110, for individual parishes]; 1862-65 [NLW Minor Deposit 577-808].

1885-1918
Cardiganshire. BL None; **NLW** 1896, 1910, 1915.

1918-1948
Cardiganshire. BL 1937-38, 1947-48; **NLW** 1918, 1920, 1924, 1932, 1935-36, 1939, 1945.

Cardiganshire continued

Boroughs Constituency
Cardigan District of Boroughs, *1832-1885*
(Aberystwyth, Adpar, Cardigan, and Lampeter).
BL 1849-63; *TNA* 1871 (incl. Pontstephan);
CA: *Aberystwyth* 1839-40, 1845, 1847, 1863;
Cardigan 1834-37, 1840, 1842-43, 1845-46, 1865,
1871; *NLW*: *Aberystwyth* 1841, 1848 [Gogerddan];
1885 [NLW MS 19644D]; 1911-13; *Lampeter* 1852,
1865 [Falcondale 136-7].

Burgess Rolls
Cardigan. *CA* 1774, 1813 [CDM/3/2-4]; 1833, 1844,
1854; *NLW* 1767-1835 [NLW Minor Deposit 490-98].

Burgess Lists
Aberystwyth. *NLW* 1907-7, 1910-13.
Adpar and Emlyn. *NLW* c.1820 [Gogerdan
uncatalogued].
Cardigan. *CA* 1835-36; 1838-39 (St. Mary's and
St. Dogmells only); 1839-40, 1841 (St. Mary's,
St. Dogmells); 1845 (St. Mary's).

Freeholders
Cardiganshire. *GL* 1780.

Freemen
Lampeter. *CA* 1837.

Ten pounds Householders
Cardigan. *CA* 1835, 1844.

Some post-1948 ER holdings at *BL* (all), *CA*.

CARMARTHENSHIRE

Abbreviations
BL = British Library.
CAS = Carmarthenshire Archives Service,
Carmarthen.
Note. Asterisked items in the Mansel Lewis
collection, available only by permission.
NLW = National Library of Wales, Aberystwyth.
SoG = Society of Genealogists.
TNA = The National Archives, Library.

County Constituencies
1832-1885
Carmarthenshire. *BL* 1862-64; *TNA* 1872;
CAS 1831* [sic]; 1832 (incomplete), 1833, 1835,
1837, 1853, 1856; 1857 (Llandilofawr only).

1885-1918
Carmarthenshire, Eastern Div. *BL* 1885/86, 1897;
CAS 1905-06; 1895, 1908 (both Llandilofawr only);
NLW 1915.
Carmarthenshire, Western Div. *BL* 1885/86, 1897;
NLW 1915; *CAS* 1888, 1892 (both Llanstephen
[?Llanstephan] only)

Carmarthenshire continued

1918-1948
Carmarthenshire, Carmarthen Div. *BL* 1937-38,
1947-48; *CAS* 1918; AVL 1918-20; 1939, 1945-48
(1945 incl. service voters); *NLW* 1918, 1929, 1947.
Carmarthenshire, Llanelly Div. *BL* 1937-38, 1947-48;
CAS 1918-28 (incl. AVL 1918-20), 1930-34, 1936-
1939, 1945 (incl. services) -1948;
NLW 1918, 1929, 1948;

Boroughs Constituency
Carmarthen District of Boroughs, *1832-1918*
(Carmarthen, Llanelly). *BL* 1858, 1863, 1885;
TNA 1871; *NLW* 1912, 1915;
CAS n.d. (19th century)*; Llanelly 1835*.

Burgess Roll (?)
Carmarthen Borough. *NLW* 1825 [Glansevin 6].

Freeholders (?)
Carmarthenshire. *NLW*: early 18th century (11
named parishes) [Edwinsford 4 1951]; mid 19th
century (Llanllwni, Llansawel, Llanbyther, Llancrwys,
Pencarreg) [Falcondale 115-9].

Parochial Registers
Carmarthenshire. *CAS* 1905-06.

Urban Sanitary voters
Boroughs (Carmarthen and Llanelly). *CAS* 1904-05.

Some post-1948 ER holdings at *BL* (all), *CAS*.

DENBIGHSHIRE

Abbreviations
BL = British Library.
DRO = Denbighshire Record Office, Ruthin.
NLW = National Library of Wales, Aberystwyth.
TNA = The National Archives, Library.
UCC = University College, Cardiff (Salisbury
Library).
UWM = University of Wales, Bangor (Dept. of
Manuscripts).

County Constituencies
1832-1885
Denbighshire. *BL* 1849-64; *TNA* 1874, 1875;
DRO 1832-44, 1846-50, 1852-54, 1856-85;
NLW 1832, 1836-37, 1839-41, 1845, 1847, 1852;
1834, 1840 (both Ruabon only) [Wynnstay L.918,
1036]; 1855 [Wynnstay 1092]; *UCC* 1834; *UWM*
c.1831(?) (parish of Llandrillo in Rhos only); 1832
(parish of Llansantffrid Glan Conwy only) [Mostyn
7873-4].

1885-1918
Denbighshire, Eastern Div. *BL* 1885/86-1915;
DRO 1886-1908, 1910-14; 1915 (incomplete);
NLW 1915.
Denbighshire, Western Div. *BL* 1885/86-1915;
DRO 1886-1915; *NLW* 1915.

Denbighshire continued

1918-1948
Denbighshire, Denbigh (Western) Div. *BL* 1918-31, 1937-38, 1947-48; *NLW* 1918/9, 1929-39, 1945; *DRO* 1918-21 (incomplete); 1923; 1927-29 (incomplete); 1930 (draft); 1931, 1933-38, 1939, 1945-48;.

Denbighshire, Wrexham (Eastern) Div. *BL* 1918-31, 1937-38, 1947-48; *NLW* 1918/9, 1929-39, 1945; *DRO* 1918, 1920, 1922 (incomplete); 1923-1925; 1927-33 (incomplete); 1934-39, 1945.

Boroughs Constituency
Denbigh District of Boroughs, *1832-1918*
(Denbigh, Holt, Ruthin and Wrexham).
BL 1863; 1897 (Denbigh and Holt only);
DRO 1835-79 (drafts: Denbigh only) [BD/A/257-305]; 1909 (Denbigh and Henllan districts).

Burgess Rolls
Denbigh. *NLW* 1699 [Chirk Castle C.6];
DRO 1701-1834 [BD/A/6-11].
Holt. *NLW* 1726-41 [Chirk Castle C.25-52].

Freeholders
Denbighshire. *DRO* 1741 [DD/WY/6759]; *NLW* ?18th century; 1741 [Wynnstay L.1292-3; 185, 1298].

Some post-1948 ER holdings at *BL* (all), *DRO*.

FLINTSHIRE

Abbreviations
BL = British Library.
FRO = Flintshire Record Office, Hawarden.
NLW = National Library of Wales, Aberystwyth.
TNA = The National Archives, Library.
UWM = University of Wales, Bangor (Dept. of Manuscripts - Mostyn Collection).

County Constituency

1832-1885
Flintshire. *BL* 1844-85; *TNA* 1874; *FRO* 1832 (photocopy); 1840 (MF); 1855, 1868-69; *NLW* 1840, 1874-75/, 1877/8; 1833 [NLW MS 5947F]; *UWM* 1832 (draft: parishes of Whitford, Tsceifiog, Nerquis, Holywell, Hawarden, Halkin, Caerwys, Llanasa, Cilcain, Nannerch, Northrop, Mold, Tryddin) [8164-83]; 1832 [8184]; 1835 (Whitford only) [8286]; 1836 Holywell (draft: property qualifs.), Y Sceifog, Whitford, Dymerchion, Caerwys, Llanasa (drafts) [8329-43]; 1838 (draft: out-voters) [8376-8]; 1841 (draft) (?county) [8380], out-voters [8383]; 1853 (draft: Whitford only) [8385].

Flintshire continued

1885-1918
Flintshire. *BL* 1885-1901; *FRO* 1912-15; *NLW* 1894, 1897, 1904, 1906, 1915.

1918-1948
Flintshire. *BL* 1937-38, 1947-48; *NLW* 1918, 1929, 1945/6, 1947/8; *FRO* 1918-39, 1945-1948.

Boroughs Constituency
Flint District of Boroughs, *1832-1918*
(Caergwyle/Caergwrle, Caerwys, Flint, Holywell, Mold, Overton, Rhuddlan and St Asaph) *BL* 1863-85, 1887, 1891-1892, 1895, 1897-98, 1904, 1906; *TNA* 1875; *NLW* 1875/5, 1897, 1904, 1906; *FRO* 1836-56, 1874, 1877, 1894, 1897, 1904 (all MF); *UWM* (drafts): 1832 (Caerwys, Holywell and Greenfield, Mold) [8166, 8177, 8182]; 1836 [8339]; 1837 (Gwaunyscor onlky) [8346]; 1838 (Caerwys only) [8375]; ?1839 (Caerwys only) [8379].

Burgess Rolls (?)
Caergwrle. *FRO* 1733.
Caerwys. *NLW* 1740-42 [Wynnstay L.828, 829].
Flint. *NLW* early 18th century [Hawarden 1916]; *FRO* 1835-59.
Flint (and Overton). *NLW* 1741 [Wynnstay 811].
Flint (and Coleshill Fawr, Overton and Caergwrle, Overton and Knolton). *NLW* 1807 [Glynne of Hawarden 5008, 5073, 5123, 4980, 5074, 5013, 4979].
Overton. *NLW* c.1861 [Wynnstay L.1026].

Freeholders
Flintshire. *NLW* early 18th century (named parishes) [Hawarden 1916]; first half of 19th century [NLW MSS 6319-21E]; *UWM* n.d. (pre-1763) [7890]; n.d. (18th century) [7898]; 1831 [8152].

Jury Lists
Caerwys (Manor of). *UWM* 1741-54 [6181-95].

Some post-1948 ER holdings at *BL* (all), *FRO*.

GLAMORGAN

Abbreviations

AL = Aberdare Library.
BL = British Library.
CLS = Cardiff Central Library, Local Studies.
CU = Cardiff University, Salisbury Library.
GL = Guildhall Library, London.
GRO = Glamorgan Record Office, Cardiff.
NLW = National Library of Wales, Aberystwyth.
MTL - Merthyr Tydfil Central Library
SCL = Swansea Central Library.
SoG = Society of Genealogists.
TNA = The National Archives, Library.

County Constituencies

1832-1885

Glamorganshire. *BL* 1843-49, 1851, 1853, 1857-78, 1880-81, 1883-85; *TNA* 1874; *NLW* 1845-46/7, 1857/8, 1868/9; *GRO* c.1832, c.1840, 1843-59, 1863-65, 1867, 1869-74, 1876-79, 1881-1885; Rhondda 1840-85; *CU* 1844-45, 1852, 1868; *SCL* 1845; *GL* 1845, 1851; 1871 (incomplete) *CLS* 1845/6 (with index by Glamorgan FHS).

1885-1918

Glamorganshire, Eastern Div. *BL* 1885/86-1915; *NLW* 1889-93, 1896-99, 1902-05, 1908-11, 1915; *GRO* 1885-1914; *MTL* 1888, 1890, 1892, 1895, 1898, 1900, 1902, 1905, `907, 1911, 1913, 1915.
Glamorganshire, Mid Div. *BL* 1885/86-1915; *NLW* 1669-93, 1896-1905, 1908-12, 1915; *GRO* 1885-1914.
Glamorganshire, Rhondda Div. *BL* 1885/86-1915; *NLW* 1888-93, 1896-1913, 1915; *GRO* 1885-1914.;
Glamorganshire, Southern Div. *BL* 1885/86-1915; *NLW* 1890-93, 1896-1911, 1915; *GRO* 1885-1915; *CLS* 1885-6.
Glamorganshire, Western or Gower Div. *BL* 1885/86-1915; *NLW* 1889-93, 1896-1912; *GRO* 1885-1914.

1918-1948

Glamorganshire, Aberavon Div. *BL* 1919-31, 1937-1938, 1947-48; *GRO* 1918-29, .1931-39, 1945-48 (incl. service voters); *NLW* 1918, 1929.
Glamorganshire, Caerphilly Div. *BL* 1919-31, 1937-1938, 1947-48; *GRO* 1918-29, 1931-39, 1945-48 (incl. service voters); *NLW* 1918, 1929.
Glamorganshire, Gower Div. *BL* 1919-31, 1937-1938, 1947-48; *GRO* 1918-39, 1945-48 (incl. service voters); *NLW* 1929.
Glamorganshire, Llandaff and Barry Div. *BL* 1919-1931, 1937-1938, 1947-48; *GRO* 1918-29, 1931-39, 1945-48; *NLW* 1918, 1929; *CLS* 1924-39, 1945-48 (possible gaps).
Glamorganshire, Neath Div. *BL* 1919-31, 1937-1938, 1947-48; *GRO* 1918-39, 1945-48 (incl. service voters); *NLW* 1918, 1929.
Glamorganshire, Ogmore Div. *BL* 1919-31, 1937-1938, 1947-48; *GRO* 1918-39, 1945-48 (incl. service voters); *NLW* 1918, 1929.

Glamorganshire, Pontypridd Div. *BL* 1919-31, 1937-1938, 1947-48; *GRO* 1918-39, 1945-48 (incl. service voters); *NLW* 1918, 1929.

Boroughs Constituencies

Cardiff District of Boroughs (incl. Cowbridge and Llantrisant). *1832-1918*. *BL* 1880-82, 1884-1915; *GL* 1851; *CLS* 1847-1908 (missing 1879, 1890, 1905, 1907), 1914.
Cardiff, Central Div., *1918-48*. *BL* 1918-31, 1937-38, 1947-48; *NLW* 1918, 1929; *CLS* 1918-39, 1945-48.
Cardiff, East Div., *1918-48*. *BL* 1918-31, 1937-38, 1947-48; *CLS* 1918-39, 1945-48.
Cardiff, South Div., *1918-48*. *BL* 1918-31, 1937-38, 1947-48; *CLS* 1918-39, 1945-48.
Merthyr Tydfil, *1832-1918*. *BL* 1851-63, 1870-1906; *GRO* 1840-1907 (Aberdare 1840-1913); *NLW* 1872 [NLW MS 11691E]; 1886, 1915; *MTL* 1832, 1868, 1871, 1873, 1875, 1878, 1885, 1890, 1900, 1904, 1906; *AL* 1879, 1889 (Aberdare parish) 1890, 1895, 1900, 1904 (Aberdare, Llanwyno, Merthyr and Vaynor parishes [MF]), 1915 (Aberdare and Llanwyno).
Merthyr Tydfil, Aberdare Div. *1918-48*. *BL* 1918-Spring 1924, Spring 1925-31, 1937-38. 1947-48; *GRO* 1931-39, 1945-48; *AL* 1918-19 (incl. AVL), 1938-9, 1945-47 (also 1919, 1936 Aberdare and Llanwyno, 1930, 1932, 1934-35 for Aberdare parish)
Merthyr Tydfil, Merthyr Div. *1918-48*. *BL* 1918-31, 1937-38. 1947-48; *MTL* 1918-20, 1922, 1925, 1926-1932, 1935, 1939, 1946-48.
Rhondda East Div. *1918>* *BL* 1937-38, 1947>; *NLW* 1929, 1945 (incomplete); *Treorchy Library* 1918-39, 1945-48.
Rhondda West Div. *1918>* *BL* 1937-38, 1947>; *NLW* 1929, 1945 (incomplete); *Treorchy Library* 1918-29, 1945-48.
Swansea District of Boroughs (Aberavon, Kenfig, Lougher, Neath and Swansea)t). *1832-1885.* *BL* 1868; *TNA* (Loughor, Neath) 1874; *GRO* 1840-1885.
Swansea District of Boroughs, Swansea District Div. (Swansea [lesser], Aberavon, Kenfig, Lougher, Neath). *1885/86-1918*. *BL* none; *GRO* 1885-88; *SCL* 1907-15.
Swansea District of Boroughs, Swansea Town Div. (the major part of Swansea). *1885/86-1918.* *BL* none; *GRO* 1885-88; *SCL* 1907-15.
Swansea, East Div. *1918>*. *BL* 1937-39, 1947>; *SCL* 1921, 1926, 1936 (parts only); 1938, 1945>; *NLW* 1918.
Swansea, West Div. *1918>*. *BL* 1937-39, 1947>; *SCL* 1921, 1926, 1936 (parts only); 1938, 1945>; *NLW* 1918, 1929.

University of Wales 1918-48

BL None; *GRO* 1938; *CLS* 1931.

Glamorgan continued

Burgess Rolls

Aberavon. *BL* 1888; *GRO* 1888-92;
 Port Talbot Reference Library 1861-82 (MS).
Cardiff. *CLS* 1850-1914; *SoG* 1826.
Combridge. *GRO* 1888-1913.
Llantrisant. *NLW* 1778, 1783, 1785, 1817 [Bute 3276,
 2505-7, 2512].
Neath. *GRO* 1888-92.
Swansea. *SCL* 1836, 1874-75, 1878-80, 1882, 1884.

Parochial Registers

Cardiff Borough. *CLS* 1894-1904.

Post-1948 ER holdings at *BL* (all); *NLW, GRO; CLS,
SCL; Aberdare; Mid-Glamorgan: Bridgend; Neath,*
and *Port Talbot Reference Libraries.*

MERIONETH (Merionnydd)

Abbreviations
BL = British Library.
MA = Merioneth Archives (Archifdy Meironnydd),
    Bala Road, Dolgellau.
NLW = National Library of Wales, Aberystwyth.
TNA = The National Archives, Library.
UWM = University of Wales (Dept. of Manuscripts),
    Bangor.

County Constituency
1832-1948

Merionethshire. *BL* 1859-63, 1885/86, 1889-1915,
Aut. 1921, 1937-38, 1947-48.; *TNA* 1874; *MA* 1905-
1907, 1909-11, 1914-15, 1918-39, 1945-48;
NLW 1837, 1851-53, 1855, 1857-59, 1860-62, 1863-
1864, 1884-86, 1915, 1918, 1929, 1932-39, 1945-
1948; 1832 [Peniarth deeds 514]; mid-19th century
[Longueville 1355 (fragment)].

Freeholders

County. *UWM* (*Mostyn Collection*) 1774 (Hundreds of
Edeyrnion, Penllyn, Mawddwy, Esimanner, Tal-y-
Bont, Ardudwy [8405, 8407-16]; Plas Hen only
[8417]); n.d. (18th century) some leasehold and
freehold voters [8418].

Post-1948 ER holdings at *BL* (all); *NLW, MA.*

MONMOUTHSHIRE (Gwent)

Abbreviations
BL = British Library.
CLS = Cardiff Central Library, Local Studies.
GRO = Gwent Record Office, Cwmbran.
NCL = Newport Central Library.
NLW = National Library of Wales, Aberystwyth.
    Note. Stray Electoral registers, Burgess rolls and
    Freemen lists in the Sir Leonard Twiston-Davies and
    other collections may be undifferentiated in the
    N.L.W. catalogue.
SoG = Society of Genealogists.
TNA = The National Archives, Library.

County Constituencies
1832-1885

Monmouthshire. *BL* None; *TNA* 1874; *SoG* 1847;
 GRO 1832; 1834-36 (MS); 1837-40, 1843-44, 1846-
 1847; 1848 (MS); 1849, 1852-56, 1858-63, 1865;
 1868-84 (incomplete); *NCL* 'c.1830'; 1840, 1843-44,
 1848, 1852-53, 1855, 1865; 1868 (with MS votes
 cast); 1874-76, 1878-79; *CLS* 1847, 1868;
 NLW 1839, 1843/4-1844/5, 1846/7, 1848/9, 1852/3-
 1856/7, 1858/9-1860/1, 1863/4, 1865/6, 1868-70,
 1870-72, 1874-79, 1881; 1835, 1840, 1845-46; 1851
 [Tredegar Park 71/712]; 1868 [T Pk 20/71]; the
 Twiston-Davies collection includes what are probably
 electoral registers for the following places:
 Cwmcarvan, 1846; Dingestow, 1846; Dixton, c.1832,
 1834, 1836, 1846, 1851; Grosmont, 1835, 1846;
 Llandeilo Crosenny, 1844; Llandogo, 1846;
 Llanfihangel Yestern Lewern, 1838, 1845-46;
 Llangattock Vibon Avel, 1846; Penallt, 1846;
 Penrose, 1841, 1845; Rockfield, 1836, 1845-46; St
 Maughan, 1846; Skenfrith, 1845-46; Tregane, 1846,
 Trelleck, 1841, 1846.

1885-1918

Monmouthshire, Northern Div. *BL* 1885/86-1915;
 GRO 1885-1908, 1910-15; *NLW* 1887-1915;
 NCL 1888-89, 1891, 1894, 1896, 1899-1900, 1903-
 1909, 1915; *CLS* 1896, 1899, 1904-08, 1915.
Monmouthshire, Southern Div. *BL* 1885/86-1915;
 GRO 1885-1908, 1910-15; *NLW* 1887-1915;
 NCL 1888-89, 1891, 1894, 1896, 1900, 1903, 1905,
 1907, 1909, 1911-12, 1915;
 CLS 1905, 1907, 1909, 1915.
Monmouthshire, Western Div. *BL* 1885/86-1915;
 GRO 1890-1915; *NLW* 1887-1915; *NCL* 1888-89,
 1894, 1896, 1900, 1903, 1905, 1907, 1910-15;
 CLS 1910-15.

1918-1948

Monmouthshire, Abertillery Div. *BL* 1918-39, 1937-
 1938, 1947-48; *GRO* 1918-39, 1945-48;
 NLW 1918-39, 1945; *NCL* 1922-39, 1945-48.
Monmouthshire, Bedwellty Div. *BL* 1918-31, 1937-
 1938, 1947-48; *GRO* 1918-39, 1945-48;
 NLW 1918-39, *NCL* 1922-39, 1945-48.
**Monmouths
hire, Ebbw Vale Div.** *BL* 1918-31, 1937-1938, 1947-
 48; *GRO* 1918-39, 1945-48;
 NLW 1918-39, *NCL* 1922-39, 1945-48.

Monmouthshire: *County 1918-1948* continued

Monmouthshire, Monmouth Div. *BL* 1918-31, 1937-1938, 1947-48; *GRO* 1918-39, 1945-48; *NLW* 1918-39, *CLS* 1946 (Rumney only); *NCL* 1922-39, 1945-48.

Monmouthshire, Pontypool Div. *BL* 1918-31, 1937-1938, 1947-48; *GRO* 1918-39, 1945-48; *NLW* 1918-39, *NCL* 1922-39, 1945-48.

Boroughs Constituency

Monmouth District of Boroughs (Monmouth, Newport and Usk). *1832-1918*. *BL* 1869 (?or 1870), 1882-1885/86; *GRO* 1845, 1847, 1849, 1856, 1861; *NCL* 1845-47, 1849, 1851, 1854, 1856, 1858-62, 1868, 1882, 1884-85; (?Monmouth only) 1885-90, 1893, 1903-05, 1907-08; Newport: 1906 (overseers' list); 1914 (and draft); CLS 1868; *NLW* 1835 (Newport and St. Woolos); 1846 (Newport and Nevern [Pemb.]) [Llwyngwair 14,294], 1852 (Usk); Monmouth (Boroughs?). '1830-1834', 1835 (with Dixton); 1836, 1840-41, 1846, 1851-52, 1885 [possibly duplicated entry].

Newport. *1918>.* *BL* 1937-38, 1947>; *GRO* 1924, 1926-39; *NCL* 1918 (and draft); 1919-39, 1945>; AVL 1918-19, '1921>'.

Burgess Rolls

Monmouth, Newport, Usk. *GRO* 1747, 1773-1878 (all MS); **Newport** only: 1838, 1883, 1885-92, 1894-1908, 1910-13.

Newport (West Ward). *NCL* 1871-72, 1910 (part); 1914, 1922-39, 1945>; *NLW* 1945.

Burgess Lists

Monmouth, Newport, Usk. *GRO* 1780-1818 (MS); 1835 (with MS votes cast); 1860, 1869, 1873; and n.d.

Newport. *NLW* 1741-55, 1819, 1832.

Freeholders

County. *NLW* early 18th century [Tredegar Park 117/355]; 1771 [T Pk 66/46-80].

Abergavenny. *NLW* 1813 [T Pk 93/509].

Ragland and **Trellick, Skenfrith**: *NLW* 18th century [T Pk 53/80-81].

Wenlooge. *NLW* 1713 [T Pk 93/509].

Freemen

Monmouth, Newport, Usk. *GRO* 1832-34 (MS); 1836-1844 (Monmouth only); 1838 and n.d. (Usk only); 1843-44, 1846, 1866-68 (MS).

Property Owners

Abergavenny. *NCL* 1852.

Post-1948 ER holdings at *BL* (all); NLW, *GRO, NCL.*

See R.L. Gant, 'Electoral Registers as a guide to village structures: a study in south-east Monmouthshire [Caldicot, 1915, 1939]', *The Local Historian* **11**.1 (1974).

MONTGOMERYSHIRE

Abbreviations

BL = British Library.
Bod = Bodleian Library, Oxford.
NLW = National Library of Wales, Aberystwyth.
PAO = Powys County Archives Office, Llandrindod Wells.
TNA = The National Archives, Library.
UWM = University of Wales, Bangor (Dept. of Manuscripts).

County Constituency

1832-1918

Montgomeryshire. *BL* 1885/86; *TNA* 1875; *NLW* 1880, 1886, 1888/9, 1892, 1894-96/7, 1900, 1911, 1915; 1857 [Wynnstay L.12461]; Berriew, 1889 [Glansevern 13785]; Llandislio, 1874 [Longueville 1355]; *PAO* 1887 [Mont. Public Records Q/REe 12].

1918-1948

Montgomeryshire. *BL* 1918-21, 1937-38, 1947-48; *NLW* 1918 (incomplete), 1929, 1945-46..

Boroughs Constituency

Montgomery District of Boroughs, *1832-1918* (Llanfyllin, Llanidloes, Machynlleth, Montgomery, Newtown and Welshpool). *BL* 1854, 1860-72, 1874, 1876-88, 1890-1903, 1905, 1907-08, 1911-15; *TNA* 1872, 1874; *Bod* 1870-72, 1874, 1876-88, 1890-1903, 1905-08, 1910-15; *NLW* 1832 [Glansevern 14028-37]; 1877 [Longueville 1036]; Machynlleth, 19th century [Wynnstay L.1166]; *PAO* 1861-76 [Mont Public Records Q/REe 1-11].

Burgess Rolls

Llanfyllin and **Welshpool.** *NLW* 1678, 1678/9 [Wynnstay 85/4, L.1194-5].

Llanfyllin. *NLW* 1775-1824 [Powis Castle 22,285-9].

Llanidloes. *UWM:* certificates of election 1792-1822 [Mostyn 6235-39].

Freeholders

County. *NLW* 1774 [Powis Castle 10619, 21710].

Llanfyllin, Dythur and **Mathravel.** *NLW* 1678-79 [Wynnstay L.1194, 1196-98].

Mathravel. *NLW* 1774 [Powis Castle 21568].

Welshpool, Guilsford, Llandinio and **Llandyslio.** *NLW* late 18th century [Wynnstay L.1243].

Welshpool. *NLW* 1930, 1932 [Powysland Club 1985 deposit].

See H.R. Jones, 'A study of rural migration in Central Wales', *Trans. Inst. British Geographers* **37** (1965).

Post-1948 ER holdings at *BL* (all); *NLW.*

PEMBROKESHIRE

Abbreviations
BL = British Library.
NLW = National Library of Wales, Aberystwyth.
PmRO= Pembrokeshire Record Office, Haverfordwest.
TNA = The National Archives, Library.

County Constituency

1832-1918
Pembrokeshire. *BL* 1863-64, 1885/6; *TNA* 1871-72; *PmRO* 1836-39, 1842, 1844, 1847-49, 1851-55, 1859-1863, 1865-68, 1870-73, 1876, 1878-83, 1885, 1887; 1890 (Tegryn only); 1891-92, 1894, 1896-1901, 1903-06, 1908-09, 1911-1913, 1915; *NLW* 1831 [Eaton, Evans & Williams 11939-53, 5402-8, 5269-5383]; 1846 (Nevern and Newport [Mon.]) [Llwyngwair 14,294]; *c*.1860 (specified parishes only) [Llwyngwair 31]; 1901 [Picton Castle 4774]; 1880, 1915.

1918-1948
Pembrokeshire. *BL* 1918-21, Aut. 1923-Spr. 1926, 1927-31, 1937-38, 1947-48; *PmRO* 1918 (AVL); 1923-29, 1932, 1935-38, 1945-47 (incl. services); *NLW* 1918, 1929-31, 1945, 1946-47

Boroughs Constituency
Pembroke District of Boroughs, *1832-1885* (Milford, Pembroke, Tenby and Wiston). *BL* 1864; *TNA* 1875; *NLW* 1884 (Haverfordwest) [NLW MS 2956A] [?if borough or county?].
Pembroke and Haverfordwest District of Boroughs, *1885/86-1918* (Fishguard, Haverfordwest, Milford, Narberth, Pembroke, Tenby and Wiston). *BL* 1885/86-96, 1900, 1909, 1915.

County Council Voters
PmRO 1889, 1891, 1893-1900, 1902-07, 1909-13.

Overseers' Lists
PmRO 1832-51; 1852 (Fishguard, Haverfordwest and Brawdy only); 1853-64; 1872 (Haverfordwest only); 1878 (Wiston only).

Post-1948 ER holdings at *BL* (all); *PmRO*.

RADNORSHIRE

Abbreviations
BL = British Library.
NLW = National Library of Wales, Aberystwyth.
PAO = Powys County Archives Office, Llandrindod Wells.
TNA = The National Archives, Library.

County Constituency

1832-1918
Radnorshire. *BL* none; *TNA* 1875; *PAO* 1868-79, 1884-90, 1892-95, 1897-1902, 1904-05, 1907, 1909-1912, 1914-15 [Radnors. Q.S.]; 1876-82, 1884-85, 1892, 1913; *NLW* 1833 [Maybery 6445]; 1835 (Llandewi Ystradenni only); 1893, 1915.

1918-1948
Breconshire and Radnorshire. *BL* Aut. 1921-32, 1937-38, 1947-48; *NLW* 1918, 1929, 1945; *PAO* 1925 (householders).

Boroughs Constituency
Radnorshire District of Boroughs, *1832-1885* (Cefnyllys, Knighton, Knucklas, New Radnor, Presteign and Rhayader). *BL* none; *TNA* 1872-73; *NLW* 1835 (New Radnor) [Maybery 6764]; 1862 [Harpton Court 2223].

List of Voters
County (Painescastle and Presteigne only). 1690 *University of Nottingham,* Dept. of Manuscripts [Pw 2 Hy 408].

Post-1948 ER holdings at *BL* (all).

Abbreviations

BL = British Library.
DAC = Dumfries Archive Centre, 32 Burns Street, Dumfries DG1 2PS
GL = Guildhall Library, London.
GRA = Grampian Regional Archives, Old Aberdeen House, Dunbar Street, Aberdeen AB2 1UE.
NAS = National Archives of Scotland, Edinburgh.
NLS = National Library of Scotland, Edinburgh.
SoG = Society of Genealogists, London.
Str = Strathclyde Regional Archives, The Mitchell Library, Glasgow.

Since 1946-48 the *National Library of Scotland* has taken all Electoral Registers for Scotland. There are a few for earlier years scattered throughout the printed and card catalogues, which have been identified as far as possible. Also included are Valuation Rolls of property owners, the equivalent of ratepayers' lists:

I am most grateful to Miss Alison Lindsay and colleagues at the *National Archives of Scotland*, who have gone to great trouble to help me examine the catalogue and attempt to identify stray registers amongst their collections.

Aberdeen Burgh. NLS. Burgesses: 1399-1700 (publ., ed. A.M. Munro, New Spalding Club 6, 1890).
Aberdeen Burgh. 1832-85. BL None.
Aberdeen Burgh North. 1885>. BL 1885/6-87, 1918-1939, 1945>
Aberdeen Burgh South. 1885> BL 1885/6-87, 1918-1939, 1945>
Aberdeenshire. NLS. 1696 (*List of Pollable Persons*, ed. John Stuart, Spalding Club 39 (2 vols., 1844); freeholders: 1790, 1832; Valuation rolls: 1667 (Third Spalding Club); 1875, 1881-2, 1884-5, 1887-1927, 1932-45, 1947>.
Aberdeenshire. 1832-67. BL None; **SoG** 1832.
Aberdeenshire, Eastern. 1868-1918. BL 1885/6.
Aberdeenshire, Western. 1868-1918. BL 1885/6.
Aberdeenshire & Kincardineshire, Central. 1918-48. BL 1918-39, 1945-48; **GRA** 1918-39, 1945-48.. (see also Kincardineshire)
Aberdeenshire & Kincardineshire, Eastern. 1918-48. BL 1918-39, 1945-48; **GRA** 1918-39, 1945-48.
Aberdeenshire & Kincardineshire, Western. 1918-48. BL 1918-39, 1945-48; **GRA** 1918-39, 1945-48.
Airdrie - see Falkirk Burghs.
Annan - see Dumfries Burghs.
Anstruther, Easter and Wester - see St Andrews Burghs.
Arbroath - see Montrose Burghs.
Ardrossan - see Ayr Burghs.
Argyllshire. NLS Valuation rolls: 1872>.
Argyllshire. 1832-1948. BL 1862-88, 1937, 1947-48.

Ayr Burghs (Ardrossan [1918-48], Ayr, Campbeltown [to 1918], Inverary [to 1918], Irvine, Oban [to 1918], Prestwick [1918-48], Saltcoats [1918-48], Troon [1918-48]).
1832-1948. **BL** 1862-1914, 1918-1936, 1937, 1938 (incomplete), 1939, 1945, 1947-48.
Ayr Burgh. NLS 1933, 1935-38.
Ayrshire. NLS Valuation rolls: 1891-1942.
Ayrshire. 1832-67. BL 1862-67.
Ayrshire, Northern. 1868-1918. BL. None; **Str** 1884-1915.
Ayrshire, Southern. 1868-1918. BL. None; **Str** 1884-1915.
Ayrshire & Bute, Bute & Northern. 1918-48. BL 1937, 1947-48; **Str** 1918-38, 1945>.
Ayrshire & Bute, Kilmarnock. 1918-48. BL 1937, 1947-48; **Str** 1918-38, 1945>.
Ayrshire & Bute, South Ayrshire. 1918-48. BL 1937, 1947-48; **Str** 1918-38, 1945>; **Str** 1918-38, 1945>.
Banff - see Elgin Burghs.
Banffshire. 1832-1948. BL 1862-63, 1885/6, 1937, 1947; **GRA** 1939, 1945-48.
Banffshire. NLS Valuation rolls: 1892-1902, 1905> (from 1922 incl. burgh).
Berwick, North - see Haddington Burghs.
Berwickshire. NLS Valuation rolls: 1817, 1853.
Berwickshire, 1832-1918. BL 1885/6;
Berwickshire & Haddingtonshire. 1918-48. BL 1918-39 (incomplete except 1937), 1947-48.
Blackfriars - see Glasgow: Blackfriars & Hutchestown.
Bothwell - see Lanarkshire: Bothwell.
Brechin - see Montrose Burghs.
Bridgeton - see Glasgow: Bridgeton.
Buckhaven - see Kirkcaldy Burghs (1918-48).
Burntisland - see Kirkcaldy Burghs.
Bute - see Ayrshire.
Buteshire. 1832-1918. BL 1862-65.
Caithness. 1832-1918. BL 1862-68; **NAS** 1835, 1837 [SC14/64].
Caithness & Sutherland. 1918>. BL 1937, 1947> (see also Sutherland)
Cambeltown - see Ayr Burghs (to 1918)
Camlachie - see Glasgow: Camlachie.
Cathcart - see Glasgow: Cathcart.
Clackmannan. NLS Valuation rolls: 1888-1967.
Clackmannanshire & Kinross-shire. 1832-1918. BL 1862-63.
(see also Perthshire & Kinross-shire, Stirlingshire)
Coatbridge - see Lanarkshire: Coatbridge.
Cowdenbeath - see Dunfermlne Burghs.
Crail - see St Andrews Burghs.
Cromarty (burgh) - see Wick Burghs.
Cromarty (county) - see Ross-shire.
Cullen - see Elgin Burghs.
Cupar - see St Andrews Burghs.
Culross - see Stirling Burghs.
Dalkeith - see Midlothian.
Dingwall - see Wick Burghs.

Scotland continued

Dornoch - see Wick Burghs.

Dumbarton - see Kilmarnock Burghs.

Dumfries Burghs (Annan, Dumfries, Kirkcudbright, Lochmaben, Sanquhar). *1832-1918.*
BL 1863 (incomplete);
DAC Dumfries 1867-8, 1896 [GOLD H3/33-4];
Burgess rolls: 1887-8, 1891, 1893 [GOLD H/36, 38, 40, 42]; females 1887-8, 1891 [GOLD H/37, 39, 41]; Sanquhar. 1839, 1849, 1851, 1853 [GLD H3/50].

Dumfriesshire. *NLS* Valuation rolls: 1862, 1874, 1877, 1880-2, 1884, 1886>.

Dumfriesshire. *1832-1948.* BL 1862-71, 1874-1875, 1885-87, 1937, 1947-48; *SoG* 1868 (with poll); *DAC* 1869 [GOLD H3/35].

Dunbar - see Haddigton Burghs.

Dunbartonshire. *NLS* Freeholders: 1780 (Minutes; may not include names); Valuation rolls: 1890>.

Dunbartonshire. *1832-48.* BL 1862-1914, 1920-1939, 1945-48; *Str* 1918-39, 1945>.
NAS c.1873-c.1892 [GD.260/4/1-5].

Dundee Burgh. *1832-1948.* BL 1937, 1947-48.
Dundee Archives & Record Centre, Dundee: Dundee 1865 (MS); AVL 1919.

Dunfermline Burghs (Cowdenbeath, Dunfermline, Inverkeithing, Lochgelli). *1918>.* BL 1937, 1947>.
(for Dunfermline pre-1918 see Stirling Burghs)

Dysart - see Kirkcaldy Burghs.

Earlsferry - see Fife, Eastern.

Edinburgh (burgh). *1832-1885.* BL 1856-66, 1869-1872, 1875-77, 1879-83; *GL* 1854; *NAS* 1832 Claimants [SC39/92/1]; *SoG* 1854; *NLS* 1856-65, 1868-73, 1875-81; (all seats?:) 1885-86, 1889-1914, 1946>; Town Council. 1882-86, 1889>.

Edinburgh Central. *1885>.* BL 1885/6, 1889-1914, 1918-39, 1945, Oct. 1946>.

Edinburgh, East. *1885>.* BL 1885/6, 1889-1914, 1918-39, 1945, Oct. 1946>.

Edinburgh North. *1918>.* BL 1918-1939, 1945, Oct. 1946>.

Edinburgh South. *1885>.* BL 1885/6, 1889-1914, 1918-39, 1945, Oct. 1946>

Edinburgh West. *1885>.* BL 1885/6, 1889-1914, 1918-39, 1945, Oct. 1946>.

Edinburghshire (Midlothian). *1832-1918.*
BL 1862-65; *NLS* 1832 (as Midlothian county).
GL Dalkeith (Midlothian) 1836; *NAS* 1832 Claimants [SC39/92/1].
(see also Midlothian)

Elgin Burghs (Banff, Cullen, Elgin, Inverurie, Kintore, Peterhead). *1832-1918.* BL 1856-66, 1885/6-89, 1892 (comp. only for 1885/6).
(See also Banffshire for Banff Burgh)

Elgin (county?). *NLS* Valuation rolls: 1937-40, 1943, 1945.

Elginshire & Nairnshire. *1832-1918.* BL 1885/6-1888, 1892.
(see also Moray & Nairnshire)

Falkirk Burghs (Airdrie, Falkirk, Hamilton, Lanark, Linlithgow). *1832-1918.* BL 1863-72 (incompl.);
NAS Falkirk 1832/3-4, 1836, 1840/1, 1857 [SC.67/61/13-20,37-8] and n.d. [SC.67/61/129]; Hamilton 1864 [SC.67/61/39].
(see also Stirling & Falkirk Burghs, post 1918)

Fife. *NLS* Valuation rolls: 1864, 1872, 1875, 1877, 1879, 1881, 1883>.

Fife. *1832-1885.* BL 1863; GL 1832.
NAS Appeals 1839-61 [SC/20/80/1].

Fife, Eastern. *1885-1948.* BL 1885/6, 1937, 1947-48; *NAS* 1899-1900 (Newport only) [SC 20/80/2-3]; Earlsferry (only) 1902-04 [SC/20/80/4-7].

Fife, Western. *1885-1948.* BL 1885/6, 1937, 1947-48.
(see also Kirkcaldy Burghs pre-1885)

Forfar - see Montrose Burghs.

Forfarshire. *1832-1948.* BL 1863, 1885/6-87, 1937, 1947-48.

Forre - see Inverness Burghs.

Fortrose - see Inverness Burghs.

Fort William - see Inverness-shire

Galashiels - see Hawick Burghs.

Galloway, New - see Wigtown Burghs.

Glasgow. Mitchell Library. Burgesses and guild brethren: 1573-1846; *Str* 1613>.

Glasgow. *1832-85.* BL 1863; *Mitchell Library* 1832, 1840, 1856-1914, 1918-39, 1945> (all seats from 1885?); *Str* 1832-45, 1856-80.

See S. Nenadic, 'Record linkage and the exploration of nineteenth-century social groups: a methodological perspective on the Glasgow middle class in 1861', *Urban History Yearbook* (1987).

Glasgow, Blackfriars & Hutchestown. *1885-1918.*
BL None; *SG* 1891/2.

Glasgow, Bridgeton. *1885>.* BL Spr.1921-Aut. 1925, 1927-39, 1947>; *Str* 1920-39, 1945>.

Glasgow, Camlachie. *1885>* BL Spr.1921-Aut. 1925, 1927-39, 1947>; *Str* 1920-39, 1945>.

Glasgow, Cathcart. *1918>.* BL Spr.1921-Aut. 1925, 1927-39, 1947>; *Str* 1920-39, 1945>.

Glasgow Central. *1885-1918.* BL None.

Glasgow, College. *1885-1918.* BL None.

Glasgow, Gorbals. *1918>.* BL Spr.1921-Aut. 1925, 1927-39, 1947>; *Str* 1920-39, 1945>.

Glasgow, Govan. *1918>.* BL Spr.1921-Aut. 1925, 1927-39, 1947>; *Str* 1920-39, 1945>.

Glasgow, Hillhead. *1918>.* BL Spr.1921-Aut. 1925, 1927-39, 1947>; *Str* 1920-39, 1945>.

Glasgow, Kelvingrove. *1918>.* BL Spr.1921-Aut. 1925, 1927-39, 1947>; *Str* 1920-39, 1945>.

Glasgow, Maryhill. *1918>.* BL Spr.1921-Aut. 1925, 1927-39, 1947>; *Str* 1920-39, 1945>.

Glasgow, Partick. *1918-48.* BL Spr.1921-Aut. 1925, 1927-39, 1947>; *Str* 1920-39, 1945-48.

Glasgow, Pollock. *1918>.* BL Spr.1921-Aut. 1925, 1927-39, 1947>; *Str* 1920-39, 1945>.

Glasgow, St Rollox. *1885-1948.* BL Spr.1921-Aut. 1925, 1927-39, 1947>; *Str* 1920-39, 1945-48.

Glasgow, Shettleston. *1918>.* BL Spr.1921-Aut. 1925, 1927-39, 1947>; *Str* 1920-39, 1945>.

Scotland continued

Glasgow, Springburn. *1918>. BL* Spr.1921-Aut. 1925, 1927-39, 1947>; *Str* 1920-39, 1945>.

Glasgow, Tradeston. *1885>. BL* Spr.1921-Aut. 1925, 1927-39, 1947>; *Str* 1920-39, 1945>.

Glasgow, Port - see Kilmarnock Burghs.

Gorbals - see Glasgow: Gorbals.

Govan - see Lanarkshire: Govan (1885-1918); Glasgow: Govan (post-1918).

Grangemouth - see Stirling & Falkirk Burghs.

Greenock. *1832>. BL* 1856-63, 1937, 1947>; *Str* 1905-15, 1918-39, 1945>.

Haddington Burghs (Dunbar, Haddington, Jedburgh, Lauder, North Berwick). *1832-1918. BL* None; *NAS* North Berwick: 1833-63, 1868-88 [B56/17/742-3].

Haddingtonshire. *1832-1918. BL* 1885/6-1914.

Hamilton - see Falkirk Burghs (1832-1918); Lanarkshire: Hamilton (1918-48).

Hawick Burghs (Galashiels, Hawick, Selkirk). *1868-1918. BL* None; *NAS* Hawick, 1832-61 [SC.63/61/1-3].

Hillhead - see Glasgow: Hillhead.

Hutchestown - see Glasgow: Blackfriars & Hutchestown.

Innerleven - see Kirkcaldy Burghs.

Inverary - see Ayr Burghs (to 1918).

Inverbervie - see Montrose Burghs.

Inverkeithing - see Dunfermline Burghs (from 1918), Stirling Burghs (pre 1918).

Inverness Burgh. *NLS* Valuation rolls: 1929-30, 1935-45, 1947>.

Inverness Burghs (Forre, Fortrose, Inverness, Nairn). *1832-1918. BL* 1885/6-88, 1892 (incomplete); *NAS* Inverness. 1832-72 [SC.29/71/1-7].

Inverness-shire. *NLS* Valuation rolls: 1867, 1875, 1878, 1880, 1882-3, 1887-on;

Inverness-shire. *1832-1918. BL* None; *NAS* Fort William. 1835 [SC.29/71/15].

Inverness-shire & Ross & Cromarty: Inverness Div. *1918-48. BL* 1937 (comp.), 1947-48 (incomplete. **Ross & Cromarty Div.** *1918-48. BL* 1937, 1947-48. **Western Isles Div.** *1918-48. BL* 1937, 1947-1948.

Inverurie - see Elgin Burghs.

Irvine - see Ayr Burghs.

Jedburgh - see Haddington Burghs.

Kelvingrove - see Glasgow: Kelvingrove.

Kilmarnock - see Ayrshire & Bute.

Kilmarnock Burghs (Dumbarton, Kilmarnock, Port Glasgow, Renfrew, Rutherglen). *1832-1918. BL* None; *Str* Dumbarton 1914; Renfrew 1914; Rutherglen. 1832-55, 1876, 1906-15.

Kilrenny - see St Andrews Burghs.

Kincardineshire. *NLS* Valuation rolls: 1881-2, 1886>.

Kincardineshire. *1832-1918. BL* 1885/6; (see also Aberdeenshire).

Kinghorn - see Kirkcaldy Burghs.

Kinross-shire - see Clackmannanshire (to 1918), Perthshire (from 1918).

Kintore - see Elgin Burghs.

Kirkcaldy Burghs (Buckhaven [1918-48], Burntisland, Dysart, Kinghorn, Kirkcaldy [incl. Fife, Western], Methil & Innerleven. *1832>.* *BL* 1856, 1859-63, 1937 (incomplete), 1947>

Kirkcudbright - see Dumfries Burghs.

Kirkcudbright (Stewartry of). *NLS* Valuation rolls: 1799, 1819.

Kirkcudbrightshire. *1832-1918. BL* 1885/6; *NAS* 1832-39, 1851-62 [SC.16/68/1-5]; *DAC* Kirkcudbright. 1850-1, 1853 [GOLD H/46].

Kirkcudbrightshire & Wigtownshire. *1918-48. BL* 1937, 1947-48. (see also Wigtownshire)

Kirkwall -see Wick Burghs.

Lanark - see Falkirk Burghs (1832-1918); Lanarkshire: Lanark (1918-48).

Lanarkshire. *NLS* Valuation rolls: 1891-4, 1896>.

Lanarkshire. *1832-67. BL* 1862-67; *Duke of Hamilton c/o NRA Scotland* 1832.

Lanarkshire, Bothwell. *1918-48. BL* 1918-Spr.1919, 1920-39, 1947-48.

Lanarkshire, Coatbridge. *1918-48. BL* 1920-39, 1947-48.

Lanarkshrie, Govan. *1885-1918. BL* 1885/6-1914.

Lanarkshire, Hamilton. *1918-48. BL* 1918 (incomp.), Aut. 1919-39, 1947-48.

Lanarkshire, Lanark. *1918-48. BL* 1920-39, 1947-48.

Lanarkshire, Mid. *1885-1918. BL* 1885/6-1918.

Lanarkshire, Motherwell. *1918-48. BL* 1918-39, 1947-48.

Lanarkshire, North Eastern. *1885-1918. BL* 1885/6-1918.

Lanarkshire, North Western. *1885-1918. BL* 1885/6-1918.

Lanarkshire, Northern. *1868-85, 1918-48. BL* 1868-85, 1918, Aut. 1919-39, 1947-48.

Lanarkshire, Partick. *1885-1918. BL* 1885/6-1914.

Lanarkshire, Rutherglen. *1918-48. BL* Aut. 1919-39, 1947-48.

Lanarkshire, Southern. *1868-1918. BL* 1868-1914.

Lauder - see Haddington Burghs.

Leith Burgh. *1918-48. BL* Spr. 1921-39, 1945-1948;

Leith Burghs (Leith, Musselburgh, Portobello). *1832-1918. BL* 1858-63, 1885/6 (incomplete); *NAS* Claimants (Leith burgh only) 1832 [SC39/92/1].

Linlithgow - see Falkirk Burghs.

Linlithgowshire. *1832-1948. BL* 1862-1914, 1919-39, May 1945, 1947-48.

Lochell - see Dunfermline Burghs.

Lochmaben - see Dumfries Burghs.

Maryhill - see Glasgow: Maryhill.

Midlothian (county). *NLS* Valuation rolls: 1814, 1867, 1869, 1872-3, 1875, 1877, 1881>. see also Edinburghshire.

Midlothian & Peeblshire, Northern. *1918-48. BL* Spr. 1921-39, 1945-48 (mostly incomp.).

Midlothian & Peeblshire, Peebles & Southern. *1918-48. BL* 1932-33 (incomp.), 1937, 1947-48.

Methil & Innerleven - see Kirkcaldy Burghs.

Montrose Burghs (Arbroath, Brechin, Forfar, Inverbervie, Montrose). *1832-1948. BL* 1856-1863, 1918-37, 1947-48 (incomp. to 1936).

Moray. *NLS* Valuation rolls: 1877-78, 1881-3, 1885-6, 1890>.

62

Scotland continued

**Moray & Nairnshire. *1918-48. BL* 1937, 1947-1948.
(see also Elgin & Nairnshire)
Motherwell - see Lanarkshire: Motherwell.
Musselburgh - see Leith Burghs.
Nairn Burgh. *NLS* Valuation rolls. 1903-27, 1938>.
(see also Inverness Burghs)
Nairnshire. *NLS* Valuation rolls: 1867, 1877, 1886,
1890, 1893-1931, 1937-39, 1941>.
(see also Elgin, Moray)
New Galloway - see Wigtown Burghs.
North Berwick - see Haddington Burghs
Oban - see Ayr Burghs (to 1918).
Orkney. *NLS* Valuation rolls: 1911-40, 1945>.
**Orkney & Shetland. *1832-1918. BL* 1885/6 (incomp.)
**Orkney & Zetland. *1918>. BL* 1937, 1947>.
**Paisley. *1832>. BL* 1862-63, 1885/6, 1937, 1947>;
Str 1914-5, 1918-39, 1945>;
NLS **Paisley, Abbey** parish, voters' roll, 1840
(microfilm of printed list).
Partick - see Lanarkshire: Partick (1885-1918);
Glasgow: Partick (1918-48).
Peeblesshire. *NLS* Valuation rolls: 1888>.
**Peeblesshire. *1832-67. BL* 1862-67;
NAS 1832-61 [SC.42/44/5-7].
(see also Midlothian)
**Peeblesshire & Selkirkshire. *1868-1918.*
BL 1868-71, 1885/6.
Perth Burgh. *NLS* Valuation rolls: 1938-46, 1948>.
**Perth Burgh. *1832-1918. BL* 1856-63;
NAS 1876-77, 1892-93 c[SC49/58/3,4].
Perthshire. *NLS* Rental 1649 contrasted with
valuation 1835 (pubd. 1835); Valuation rolls: 1859,
1861, 1873-4, 1876-82, 1884, 1886-7, 1889>.
**Perthshire. *1832-1885. BL* None; *NLS* 1832;
GL 1832,.
**Perthshire, Eastern. *1885-1918. BL* None.
**Perthshire, Western. *1885-1918. BL* None.
Perthshire & Kinross-shire, Kinross & Western.
**1918-48. BL* 1937, 1947-48.
**Perthshire & Kinross-shire, Perth. *1918-48.*
BL 1937, 1947-48.
Peterhead - see Elgin Burghs.
Pittenweem - see St Andrews Burghs.
Pollock - see Glasgow: Pollock
Port Glasgow - see Kilmarnock Burghs.
Portobello - see Leith Burghs.
Prestwick - see Ayr Burghs (1918-48).
Queensferry South - see Stirling Burghs.
Renfrew - see Kilmarnock Burghs.
Renfrewshire. *NLS* Valuation rolls: 1897>
**Renfrewshire. *1832-85. BL* 1862-63;
NLS Paisley, Abbey parish, voters' roll, 1840
(microfilm of printed list)..
**Renfrewshire, Eastern. *1885-1948. BL* 1937, 1947-
1948; *Str* 1913-5, 1918-39, 1945> (incomplete).
**Renfrewshire, Western. *1885-1948. BL* 1947-1948;
Str 1913-5, 1918-39, 1945> (incomp.)
Ross & Cromarty. *NLS* Valuation rolls: 1868-1944.
**Ross-shire & Cromarty. *1832-1918. BL* None.

Roxburghshire. *NLS* Valuation rolls: 1811, 1813,
1869-70, 1873-82, 1884>.
**Roxburghshire. *1832-1918. BL* 1888-1918;
NLS 1893-1914.
**Roxburghshire & Selkirkshire. *1918-48.*
BL 1937, 1947-48; *NLS* Roxburghshire 1947>.
**Rutherglen. *Str* Burgess rolls: 1620-67, 1685, 1712,
1777-1975. See also Kilmarnock Burghs (1832-
1918); Lanarkshire: Rutherglen (1918-48)
St Andrews Burghs (Anstruther Easter and Wester,
Crail, Cupar, Kilrenny, Pittenweem, St Andrews).
1832-1918. BL 1856, 1858-63 (incomplete).
St Rollex - see Glasgow: St Rollex.
Saltcoats - see Ayr Burghs (1918-48).
Sanquhar - see Dumfries Burghs.
Selkirk - see Hawick Burghs.
Selkirkshire. *NLS* Valuation rolls: 1890>.
**Selkirkshire. *1832-67. BL* 1862-64.
NAS Selkirk (county?) 1832-61 [SC.63/61/1-3].
(see also Peeblesshire and Roxburghshire)
Shetland - see Orkney.
Shettleston - see Glasgow: Shettleston.
Springburn - see Glasgow: Springburn.
Stirling Burghs (Culross, Dunfermline, Inverkeithing,
Queensferry South, Stirling). *1832-1918. BL* 1869-
1878. 1880-1881, 1884-94 (incomp.);
NAS Stirling (Burghs?) 1832-4, 1836, 1841, 1868
[SC.67/61/5-12,81]; Dunfermline (3rd and 4th
districts) 1868 [SC.67/61/89,90].
Stirling & Falkirk Burghs (Falkirk, Grangemouth,
Stirling). *1918>. BL* 1937, 1947>.
Stirlingshire. *NLS* Valuation rolls: 1882, 1886-1910,
1912>.
**Stirlingshire. *1832-1918. BL* 1862-74, 1878-1914;
NLS 1832, 1910; *NAS* 1832-62 [SC.67/61/1-2,128];
Lennoxtown and Drymen. 1832-4, 1836, 1840-1
[SC.67/61/21-36].
**Stirlingshire & Clackmannanshire: Clackmannan &
Eastern. *1918-48. BL* 1937, 1947-48.
**Stirlingshire & Clackmannanshire: Western. *1918-
1948. BL* 1937. 1947-48.
Stranraer - see Wigtown Burghs.
**Sutherland. *1832-1918. BL* 1862-64.
(see also Caithness & Sutherland).
Tain - see Wick Burghs.
Tradeston - see Glasgow: Tradeston.
Troon - see Ayr Burghs (1918-48).
Whithorn - see Wigtown Burghs.
Wick Burghs (Cromarty, Dingwall, Dornoch, Kirkwall,
Tain, Wick). *1832-1918. BL* 1857-69, 1873-76
(incomplete); *North Highland Archives, Wick:*
Pultneytown 1894 (*NAS* 1894 MF [B73/2/3].
Wigtown Burghs (New Galloway, Stranraer, Whithorn
and Wigton). *1832-1885. BL* None.
Wigtownshire. *NLS* Valuation rolls: 1877, 1882, 1887,
1893-1932, 1936>.
**Wigtownshire. *1832-1918. BL* 1862-68, 1871,
1885/6-87; *NAS* 1832-61 [SC19/64/1.2], Upper
District, 1868 [GD.154/611].
(see also Kirkcudbrightshire)
Zetland - see Orkney.

Scotland continued

Pre-1832 printed lists of freeholders:
In Scotland from 1707 to 1832 the County voting franchise was much more restricted than in England and Wales. In 1788 there were only 2,662 voters in all. Most elections were unopposed. For the years 1788, 1790, 1811 and 1812 there are printed books listing all the freeholders county by county, showing the way they voted in the few contested elections. These are:

Sir Charles Elphinston Adam (ed.), *A View of the Political State of Scotland in the last century: A confidential report on the ... 2,662 County Voters about 1788*, Edinburgh (1887) (from a MS report to aid the Rt. Hon. William Adam of Blair Adam and Henry Erskine in managing the interests in Scotland of the Whig opposition to Pitt and Henry Dundas).

A. Mackenie, *A View of the Political State of Scotland at the late general election: Rolls of Freeholders ... as made up at the meetings for choosing their Representatives ... July 1790.*

James Bridges, *View of the Political State of Scotland at Michaelmas 1811 comprehending the rolls of the Freeholders (made up at the Michaelmas Head Counts)*, Edinburgh, John Moir (1812). In the same volume, lists made up in 1812 with names expunged or added. They were apparently altered each year at the meeting, as people had died or freeholds were bought or sold.

There are copies at **Edinburgh Central Library**, the **National Library of Scotland** and the **National Archives of Scotland**; and, for 1790 only, at the **Institute of Historical Research**, London.

IRELAND

No attempt has been made to identify pre-1922 electoral registers. The **British Library** holds electoral registers from 1922 for constituencies in Northern Ireland as shown below. The only registers held for the Republic of Ireland are for constituencies comprising the **City** and **County of Dublin** for the single year *1937*.

Co. Antrim, *1922-48. BL* 1937, 1946/49*[sic]*
Co. Armagh, *1922>. BL* 1937, 1947>
Belfast, East, *1922>. BL* 1937, 1947>
Belfast, North, *1922>. BL* 1937, 1947>
Belfast, South, *1922>. BL* 1937, 1947>
Belfast, West, *1922>. BL* 1937, 1947>
Co. Fermanagh & Tyrone. *1922-48, BL* 1937, 1947-48.
Co. Londonderry. *1922>. BL* 1937, 1947>.